THE
INTERMEDIATE CALCULUS

THE INTERMEDIATE CALCULUS

BRIJMOHAN

वाणी प्रकाशन

वाणी प्रकाशन

4695, 21-A, Daryaganj, New Delhi 110 002

Branch

Ashok Rajpath, Patna 800 004

Phone : +91 11 23273167 Fax : +91 11 23275710

www.vaniprakashan.in
vaniprakashan@gmail.com
sales@vaniprakashan.in

THE INTERMEDIATE CALCULUS
by Brijmohan

ISBN: 978-93-5229-610-1
Math

Edition 1963, 2009
Re-Print 2017

Price : ₹ 395

Printed at Tusar Colore Proses, Delhi-110 093

Vani Prakashan's signature motif is created by Artist Maqbool Fida Husain

PREFACE TO THE FIRST EDITION

Books need not be written unless they are wanted. The necessity of a book on Elementary Calculus suitable for Intermediate Class students has since long been felt. The present booklet is an endeavour to fill this gap. Thus, the object of this pamphlet is twofold : (1) to present the rudiments of Infinitesimal Calculus in as simple a form as possible ; (2) to provide a hand-book on the subject for the Intermediate Class students.

In presenting the elements of Calculus I have always begun with the idea of a limit to impress upon the student the fact that the idea of limit is fundamental and that of geometrical interpretation only secondary. This is more apparent in the case of those functions the curves of which cannot be drawn correctly.

In this small volume it should not be expected of the author to describe all the applications of Calculus. Some of the very simplest of them have been dealt with herein. This booklet pre-supposes a knowledge of Elementary Mathematics only as far as the First Year Standard. Thus, the notions of convergence and uniform convergence of series and of continuity of functions have nowhere been discussed but always taken for granted wherever necessary. At one or two places a mere mention has been made of the fact that a particular series is convergent or that a particular function is continuous so that the student may become familiar with the phrases if not with the notions.

My acknowledgments are due to many authors. But for some of the questions given herein I am chiefly indebted to Ganesh Prasad's Differential Calculus and Integral Calculus, J. Edward's Differential Calculus for Beginners and Integral Calculus for Beginners, F. S. Carey's Infinitesimal Calculus, H. S. Carslaw's Infinitesimal Calculus, Osgood's Introduction to Calculus, Todhunter's Integral Calculus and Williamson's Differential Calculus and Integral Calculus. Also, most of the questions that have recently appeared in the Intermediate Examination of the Banaras Hindu University and the Aligarh Muslim University have been included herein.

I will feel grateful for any corrections or improvements suggested.

BANARAS,
6th Dec., 1937.

BRIJ MOHAN

CONTENTS

CHAPTER I

Functions and Limits

CHAPTER II

The Differential Coefficient Applications

CHAPTER IX

INTEGRATION BY PARTS

CHAPTER X

PARTIAL FRACTIONS

CHAPTER I

FUNCTIONS AND LIMITS

1. In this booklet all angles will be supposed measured in Circular Measure, all logarithms supposed to be Napierian and all co-ordinate axes rectangular unless otherwise expressly stated.

2. The Idea of a Function.

In the equation,

$$y=2x^2+1, \qquad (2{\cdot}1)$$

if we put $x=2$, $y=9$. When $x=2\frac{1}{2}$, $y=\frac{27}{2}$ and when $x=3$, $y=19$. As we give different values to x, y goes on assuming different values.

A symbol which can take every numerical value is called a *Variable*.

A symbol which does not change its value is called a *Constant*.

In (2·1), x is a variable, 2 and 1 are constants.

Further, in (2·1), x may be given any value at pleasure, and hence is called the *Independent Variable*. The value of y depends on that of x and so y is called the *Dependent Variable*.

In (2·1), corresponding to each value of x, y has a single and definite value. A symbol which has a single and definite value for every value of x, is said to be a *Function* of x. Thus, in (2·1), y is a function of x.

We have seen that in a functional relation, the rate of change of one quantity depends upon the rate of change of another quantity. The study of this rate of change is the object of Differential calculus.

EXAMPLES OF FUNCTIONS

1. If $y=5x-8$, y has a single and definite value for every value of x. Here, y is a function of x, x is a variable and 5 and -8 are constants.

2. If $x=3\cos t+4$, x is a function of t, t is a variable and 3, 4 are constants.

3. The area A of a circle is given by the formula $A=\pi r^2$, where r is the radius of the circle. Here, r is a variable, π is a constant, and A is a function of r.

4. If $t=a\cos u+b\sin u+c$, u is a variable, a, b, c are constants, and t is a function of u.

5. Let $y=\sqrt{x}$. Here, if $x=4$, y may be $+2$ or -2. In the same way, if $x=\frac{1}{2}$, $y=\pm\sqrt{\frac{5}{2}}$. Hence the value of y corresponding to any value of x is not definite. y can assume one out of two values. So, y is not a function of x.

But, if we stipulate the condition that y is to be always positive, y has a definite value corresponding to every value of x. When $x=4$, $y=+2$; when $x=\frac{1}{2}$, $y=+\sqrt{\frac{1}{2}}$. Thus, y becomes a funtion of x.

6. Let $y=\cos^{-1}x$. (a)

If $x=\frac{1}{2}$, y may have any of the values $\frac{\pi}{3}$, $\frac{5\pi}{3}$, $\frac{7\pi}{3}$, $\frac{11\pi}{3}$, $\frac{13\pi}{3}$, $\frac{17\pi}{3}$, ...Thus, y is not a function of x. But, if we restrict y to have the least positive value consistently with (a), y becomes a function of x. In the particular case considered, y will be $\frac{\pi}{3}$

Note 1.—It is customary to use the letters a, b, c ...α, β, γ,......from the beginning of the alphabet to denote constants and the later letters $u, v, w, x, y, z, \xi, \eta$,........ to denote variables.

2. Functions are generally written as $f(x)$, $F(x)$ or $\phi(x)$.

EXAMPLES 1.

1. If $y=5x^2-2$, find the value of y when $x=0, 1, \sqrt{2}$.

2. If $f(x)=7x^2+3x-1$, find the value of $f(0)$, $f(1)$, $f(-2)$.

3. If $f(x)=ax^2+b$, calculate the value of $f(1)$, $f(-1)$, $f(0)$, $f\left(\frac{1}{a}\right)$, $f(b)$, $f\left(\frac{b}{a}\right)$.

4. If $f(x)=11$, calculate $f(2)$, $f(-2)$.

5. If $f(x)=\dfrac{x+1}{x-1}$, evaluate $f(3)$, $f(a)$, $f(2a)$.

Find (*i*) $f(x+h)$,

(*ii*) $f(x+h)-f(x)$, and

(*iii*) $\dfrac{f(x+h)-f(x)}{h}$

when

6. $f(x)=2x+3$.

7. $f(x)=x^2$.

8. A rectangle has a fixed breadth 3 cm. and a variable length x cm. Express the area of the rect. as a function of x.

9. A square has a variable side x in. Is its area a function of x ?

10. A rectangle has twice the area of the rect. given in Ex. 8. Is its area a function of x ?

11. For what values of x is the function given in Ex. (1) zero ?

3. In order that y may be a function of x, it is necessary that y should have a single, definite value for every value of x considered. Let us consider the expression

$$f(x) = \frac{x^2-4}{x-2} \qquad (\alpha)$$

Dividing out, we get $x+2$. And this expression has a definite value for every value of x. Thus $f(0)=2$, $f(1)=3$, $f(-1)=1$. And it appears that $f(2)=4$. But, here, there is one difficulty. In (α) we can divide the numerator by the denominator only when the denominator is not 0. Division by 0 is meaningless. When $x=2$, $f(x)$ assumes the form $\frac{0}{0}$ which is meaningless. We cannot first divide x^2-4 by $x-2$ and then put $x=2$ in the quotient. For, in the very act of division by $x-2$, it is assumed that $x-2$ is not to be 0.

If division by 0 were permissible, from the equation,

$$3 \times 0 = 4 \times 0,$$

we could deduce that

$$3 = 4.$$

Hence we say that in (α) $f(x)$ is not a function of x when $x=2$. In other words, the function is not defined at $x=2$.

EXAMPLES II.

Is the function

1. $\dfrac{x^3-1}{x-1}$ defined at $x=1$?

2. $\dfrac{\sin x}{x}$ defined at $x=0$?

3. $\dfrac{x^2-4}{x-2}$ defined at $x=2\dfrac{1}{1000}$?

4. $\dfrac{5x+2}{x+3}$ defined at $x=-3$?

5. $\dfrac{x^2-a^2}{x-a}$ defined at $x=a$?

6. $\dfrac{x^2-a^2}{x+a}$ defined at $x=-a$?

7. x^2-a^2 defined at $x=a$?

8. $x+a$ defined at $x=-a$?

4. The Idea of a Limit.

We have seen in § 3 that the value of the function

$$f(x)=\frac{x^2-4}{x-2}$$

does not exist for $x=2$. But suppose we give x values continuously approaching the value 2 and find out the corresponding values of $f(x)$; we get the follwoing table :

x	$f(x)$
$2\frac{1}{10}$	$4\frac{1}{10}$
$2\frac{1}{20}$	$4\frac{1}{20}$
$2\frac{1}{100}$	$4\frac{1}{100}$
$2\frac{1}{1000}$	$4\frac{1}{1000}$
$2\frac{1}{10000}$	$4\frac{1}{10000}$

A glance at this table reveals the fact that as x approaches the value 2, $f(x)$ approaches 4. In other words, as the difference between x and 2 decreases the difference between $f(x)$ and 4 decreases. A table of these differences would be instructive.

$x-2$	$f(x)-4$
$\frac{1}{10}$	$\frac{1}{10}$
$\frac{1}{20}$	$\frac{1}{20}$
$\frac{1}{100}$	$\frac{1}{100}$
$\frac{1}{1000}$	$\frac{1}{10000}$
$\frac{1}{10000}$	$\frac{1}{10000}$

As we make the difference between x and 2 smaller and smaller, the difference between $f(x)$ and 4 becomes smaller and smaller. Thus, as the quantity $(x-2)$ decreases, the quantity $[f(x)-4]$ decreases. In fact, we can make the quantity $[f(x)-4]$ as small as we please by making $(x-2)$ sufficiently small. Thus, if we want to make [$f(x)-4$] smaller than $\frac{1}{10^7}$, we have only to take a value of x lying between 2 and $2-\frac{1}{10^7}$.

Now, suppose we allot values to x which are less than 2, but continuously nearing the value 2. We shall get the following corresponding table of values :—

x	$f(x)$
$1\frac{9}{10}$	$3\frac{9}{10}$
$1\frac{99}{100}$	$3\frac{99}{100}$
$1\frac{999}{1000}$	$3\frac{999}{1000}$
$1\frac{9999}{10000}$	$3\frac{9999}{10000}$

Here, too, we observe, that the value of $f(x)$ is continuously approaching the value 4, but through values less than 4. The corresponding table of differences would be:

$x-2$	$f(x)-4$
$-\frac{1}{10}$	$-\frac{1}{10}$
$-\frac{1}{100}$	$-\frac{1}{100}$
$-\frac{1}{10000}$	$-\frac{1}{1000}$
$-\frac{1}{100000}$	$-\frac{1}{10000}$

In order to avoid any misunderstanding which may arise because of signs, let us adopt the following :—

Def. The symbol $|a-b|$ denotes the positive value of the difference between a and b.

Thus $|7-4| = 3$ and $|4-7| = 3$

With this notation, we can combine the above two tables of differences into one thus :

$\|x-2\|$	$\|f(x)-4\|$
$\frac{1}{10}$	$\frac{1}{10}$
$\frac{1}{100}$	$\frac{1}{100}$
$\frac{1}{1000}$	$\frac{1}{1000}$

So, now we can say that, by making $|x-2|$ sufficiently small, we can make $|f(x)-4|$ as small as we please. In symbolic language we write:

$$\underset{x\to 2}{\text{Lt}}\ f(x) = 4.$$

In other words, " The limit of $f(x)$, as x tends to 2, is 4. "

Generally speaking, l is the limit of $f(x)$ at $x=a$ if we can make $|f(x)-l|$ as small as we please by making $|x-a|$ sufficiently small. Thus, we shall write:

$$\underset{x\to a}{\text{Lt}}\ f(x) = l.$$

The expression '$\underset{x\to a}{\text{Lt}}$' here stands for

" The limit, as x tends to the value a, of."

EXAMPLES

1. Let a regular polygon be inscribed in a circle. Let the number of sides be increased indefinitely. Ultimately the polygon will be indistinguishable from the circle. The difference between the two will be very, very small; in fact,

smaller than any conceivable quantity, however small. We say that the circle is the limit of the polygon.

2. The difference between $\dfrac{x+2}{4x+3}$ and $\frac{2}{3}$ is $\dfrac{5x}{3(4x+3)}$ This fraction can be made smaller than any quantity we care to name by taking x sufficiently small. Hence the limit of $\dfrac{x+2}{4x+3}$ when x approaches 0, is $\frac{2}{3}$.

On the other hand, when x is increased indefinitely, the fraction is

$$\frac{1+\dfrac{2}{x}}{4+\dfrac{3}{x}}$$

which shows that it approaches the value $\frac{1}{4}$ which is therefore its limit when x is increased indefinitely. We write these results in the form

$$\underset{x\to 0}{\text{Lt}} \frac{x+2}{4x+3}=\frac{2}{3} \qquad \underset{x\to \infty}{\text{Lt}} \frac{x+2}{4x+3}=\frac{1}{4}$$

3. Let AOB be an angle $(=\theta)$ and BN perp. to OA. Then, in Circular Measure,

$$\theta=\frac{\text{Arc } AB}{OB} \quad \text{and } \sin\theta=\frac{BN}{OB}$$

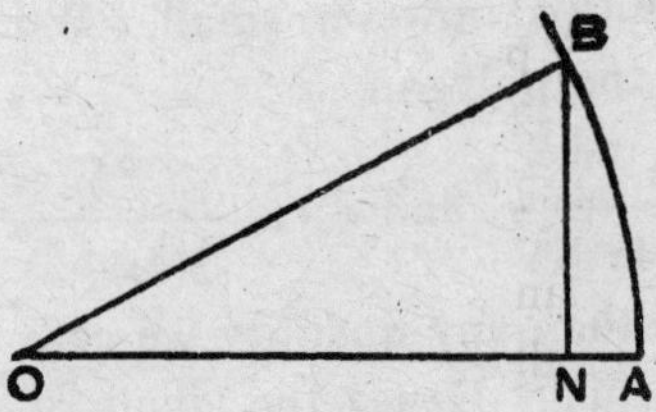

Fig. (1)

As θ becomes smaller and smaller, the difference between BN and Arc AB becomes smaller and smaller until at last either is indistinguishable from the other. So that the difference becomes smaller than any conceivable quantity.

Thus

$$\underset{\theta\to 0}{\text{Lt}}\frac{\sin\theta}{\theta}=\underset{\theta\to 0}{\text{Lt}}\frac{BN}{OB}\cdot\frac{OB}{\text{Arc } AB}=\underset{\theta\to 0}{\text{Lt}}\frac{BN}{\text{Arc } AB}=1$$

5. We give here a few important theorems on limits. Their proof is outside the scope of this book.

Let $f(x)\to A$, $\phi(x)\to B$, $\psi(x)\to C$, as $x\to a$. Then

(i) $f(x)+\phi(x)\to A+B$,

$f(x)+\phi(x)+\psi(x)+\ldots\to A+B+C+\ldots$

(ii) $f(x)-\phi(x)\to A-B$

(iii) $cf(x)\to c\,A$

(iv) $f(x)\phi(x)\to A\,B$,

$f(x)\phi(x)\,\psi(x)\ldots\to A\,B\,C\ldots$

(v) $\dfrac{f(x)}{\phi(x)}\to\dfrac{A}{B}$, provided that $B\neq O$.

In particular, $\dfrac{c}{\phi(x)}\to\dfrac{c}{B}$.

Hence, if $\phi(x)\to 1$, $\dfrac{1}{\phi(x)}\to 1$.

6. If the denominator of a fraction tends to 0, no general conclusion can be drawn about the limit of the

fraction. The limit of the fraction $\frac{x^2+1}{x}$ when $x \to o$, is

$$\underset{x \to 0}{\text{Lt}} \left(x + \frac{1}{x} \right) = \infty.$$

But we cannot say the same thing of $\underset{x \to 2}{\text{Lt}} \frac{(x-2)^2}{x^2-4}$. Here if we substitue 2 for x we get a fraction of the form $\frac{0}{0}$, which is known as an Undetermined Form. Let us put $x=2+h$, where h is a quantity, not exactly 0, but an indefinitely small quantity which continually approaches the value 0. The fraction

$$= \frac{(2+h-2)^2}{(h+2)^2-4} = \frac{h^2}{h^2+4h} = \frac{h}{h+4}$$

and the limit of this is 0, as h tends to 0.

On the other hand let us consider the limit of $\frac{x^2-9}{x-3}$ when $x \to 3$. This too assumes the form $\frac{0}{0}$. Putting $x=3+h$ as above, we see that the fraction

$$= \frac{(3+h)^2-9}{(3+h)-3} = \frac{6h+h^2}{h} = h+6.$$

So, the limit is 6.

Now, how is it that of two fractions which both assume the form $\frac{0}{0}$, one tends to 0 while the other tends to a finite limit ? The reason is not far to seek. Two quantities may be each indefinitely small but their ratio may or may not be indefinitely small.

For; the ratio depends not on their absolute but on their relative magnitudes.

Let us take two straight lines AB, ab, the one double the other, and let us bisect them at O_1, o_1.

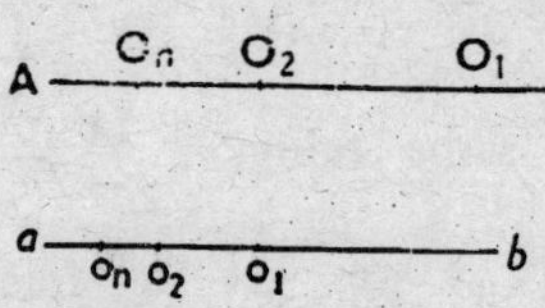

Fig. 2

The ratio $\frac{AB}{ab}=2$; so also is the ratio $\frac{AO_1}{ao_1}$.

Let us again bisect AO_1, $a\,o_1$ at O_2, o_2. The ratio $\frac{AO_2}{ao_2}$ is again equal to 2. Let us go on bisecting these lines, until at last each is diminished indefinitely. But the ratio $\frac{AO_n}{ao_n}$ is still equal to 2, even though both the numerator and denominator are indefinitely small. In fact,

$$\frac{AO_n}{ao_n}=\frac{\frac{1}{2^n}.\,AB}{\frac{1}{2^n}ab}$$

As we increase n, the numerator and the denominator go on decreasing, but their ratio remains 2. And this agrees with our notion of a ratio. A ratio remains unaltered if we multiply the numerator and denominator by the same quantity.

$$\frac{a}{b} = \frac{pa}{pb}.$$

Hence if p is a small quantity, both the numerator and denominator are very small in magnitude. But their ratio is always $\frac{a}{b}$ and so the value of the ratio depends not upon p but upon a and b. If $\frac{a}{b}$ is finite, that ratio is finite.

To sum up, then, we see that if the denominator of a fraction approaches the value 0, the limit of the fraction may be 0, a finite quantity, or ∞.

7. **Solved Examples.**

(1) Find the value of $\underset{x \to 1}{\text{Lt}} \frac{x^2-3x+2}{2x^2+x-3}$

$$\text{The fraction} = \frac{(x-1)(x-2)}{(x-1)(2x+3)}$$

Putting $1+h$ for x, where h is a small quantity, we have

$$\frac{(x-1)(x-2)}{(x-1)(2x+3)} = \frac{h(h-1)}{h(2h+5)} = \frac{h-1}{2h+5}.$$

This fraction "tends to" the value $-\frac{1}{5}$ as h approaches the value 0. Hence the limit required is $-\frac{1}{5}$.

(2) Evaluate $\underset{x \to 0}{\text{Lt}} \dfrac{x}{\sqrt{(1+x)}-1}$ (Banaras 1946)

As x is small, we may suppose it to be less than 1. Hence, applying the Binomial Theorem, we have

$$\frac{x}{(1+x)^{1/2}-1} = \frac{x}{(1+\frac{1}{2}x-\frac{1}{8}x^2+\dots)-1}$$

$$= \frac{x}{\frac{1}{2}x - \frac{1}{8}x^2 + \text{higher powers of } x}$$

$$= \frac{1}{\frac{1}{2} - \frac{1}{8}x + \dots} = \frac{1}{\frac{1}{2}} = 2.$$

(3) Evaluate $\underset{x \to \infty}{\text{Lt}} \dfrac{px + \dfrac{q}{x}}{rx + \dfrac{s}{x}}$

$$\text{The limit} = \underset{x \to \infty}{\text{Lt}} \frac{p + \dfrac{q}{x^2}}{r + \dfrac{s}{x^2}} = \frac{p}{r}$$

EXAMPLES III.

1. Find the value of $\dfrac{x^3 - p^3}{x - p}$ *when* $x \to p$.

2. Evaluate $\underset{\theta \to 0}{\text{Lt}} \cos \theta$.

3. Evaluate $\underset{x \to -\frac{2}{3}}{\text{Lt}} \dfrac{3x^2+5x+2}{3x^2-4x-4}$

4. Find $\underset{x \to b}{\text{Lt}} \dfrac{2x^2-(2b+1)x+b}{(b+1)x-b-x^2}$

5. Find $\dfrac{px+q}{qx \pm p}$ (1) when $x \to 0$ (2) when $x \to \infty$.

6. Find Lt $\dfrac{(ax+b)^2}{x^2}$ (1) when $x \to 0$ (2) when $x \to \infty$.

7. Find $\underset{x \to 1}{\text{Lt}} \dfrac{x+2\sqrt{x}-3}{x+\sqrt{x}-2}$

8. Some Important Limits.

I $\quad \underset{x \to 0}{\text{Lt}} \dfrac{\text{Sin } \theta}{\theta} = 1$ (Banaras 1948, 1952) $\underset{x \to 0}{\text{Lt}} \text{Cos } \theta = 1$

II $\quad \underset{x \to \infty}{\text{Lt}} \left(1 + \dfrac{1}{x}\right)^x = \underset{t \to 0}{\text{Lt}} (1+t)^{1/t} = e.$

$$\underset{x \to \infty}{\text{Lt}} \left(1 + \frac{a}{x}\right)^x = ea$$

III $\quad \underset{x \to 1}{\text{Lt}} \dfrac{x^n - 1}{x-1} = \underset{t \to 0}{\text{Lt}} \dfrac{(1+t)^n - 1}{t} = n.$

IV $\quad \underset{x \to 0}{\text{Lt}} \dfrac{a^x - 1}{x} = \log_e a.$

Proof of III. Let $x = 1+h$, where h tends to 0, as x approaches the value 1. Then

$$\underset{x\to 1}{\text{Lt}} \frac{x^n - 1}{x - 1} = \underset{h\to 0}{\text{Lt}} \frac{(1+h)^n - 1}{h}$$

As h approaches the value 0, we may suppose it to be less than 1. Hence, applying the Binomial Theorem we have

$$\underset{x\to 1}{\text{Lt}} \frac{x^n - 1}{x - 1} = \underset{h\to 0}{\text{Lt}} \frac{\left\{1 + nh + \frac{n(n-1)}{2!}h^2 + \dots\right\} - 1}{h}$$

$$= \underset{h\to 0}{\text{Lt}} \left\{ n + \frac{n(n-1)}{2!} h + \dots\dots\dots \right\} = n.$$

Proof of IV $\quad \underset{x\to 0}{\text{Lt}} \dfrac{a^x - 1}{x}$

$$= \underset{x\to 0}{\text{Lt}} \frac{1}{x}\left[\left\{ 1 + x \log_e a + \frac{x^2 (\log_e a)^2}{2!} + \dots \right\} - 1\right]$$

$$= \underset{x\to 0}{\text{Lt}} \left\{ \log_e a + \frac{x}{2!}(\log_e a)^2 + \dots \right\}$$

$$= \log_e a\text{*}$$

9. Other Undetermined Forms are $0 \times \infty$, $\dfrac{\infty}{\infty}$, $\infty - \infty$, 0^0, ∞^0, $1.\infty$ but by special artifices they may all be made to depend upon the form $\frac{0}{0}$.

In case x is to become infinite, it is sometimes useful to put $x = \dfrac{1}{y}$, so that when $x \to \infty$, $y \to 0$.

* In these examples we have tacitly made use of the fact that the series concerned are convergent.

Use may be made of the following important results in solving questions.

$$(1+x)^n=1+nx+\frac{n(n-1)}{2!}x^2+\frac{n(n-1)(n-2)}{3!}x^3+\ldots\ldots,$$

$$(1-x)^{-n}=1+nx+\frac{n(n+1)}{2!}x^2+\frac{n(n+1)(n+2)}{3!}x^3+\ldots\ldots,$$

$$a^x=1+x\log_e a+\frac{x^2(\log_e a)^2}{2!}+\frac{x^3(\log_e a)^3}{3!}+\ldots\ldots,$$

$$a^x=1+x+\frac{x^2}{2!}+\frac{x^3}{3!}+\ldots\ldots\ldots\ldots\ldots,$$

$$\log_e(1+x)=x-\frac{x^2}{2}+\frac{x^3}{3}-\frac{x^4}{4}+\ldots\ldots,$$

$$-\log_e(1-x)=x+\frac{x^2}{2}+\frac{x^3}{3}+\frac{x^4}{4}+\ldots\ldots,$$

$$\log_e\frac{+x}{1-x}=x+\frac{x^3}{3}+\frac{x^5}{5}+\ldots\ldots$$

10. Solved Examples.

(i) Evaluate $\underset{x\to\infty}{\text{Lt}}\ 3^x\sin\dfrac{a}{3^x}$ (Banaras 1951.)

The fraction is of the form $\infty \times 0$. The limit

$$= \underset{x\to\infty}{\text{Lt}} \; a.\frac{\sin \dfrac{a}{3^x}}{\dfrac{a}{3^x}} = a \underset{\theta\to 0}{\text{Lt}} \frac{\text{Sin } \theta}{\theta} = a.$$

(ii) Evaluate $\underset{x\to 1}{\text{Lt}} (2-x)^{1/(1-x)}$

This is of the form 1^{∞}. Putting $x=1-y$, we get

$$\underset{x\to 1}{\text{Lt}} (2-x)^{1/(1-x)} = \underset{y\to 0}{}(1+y)^{1/y} = e.$$

(iii) Evaluate

$$\underset{x\to\infty}{\text{Lt}} \frac{2x}{\sqrt{(1+x)}}$$

This is of the form $\frac{\infty}{\infty}$. Putting $x=\frac{1}{y}$ we see that the limit

$$= \underset{y\to 0}{\text{Lt}} \frac{2y}{\sqrt{(1+y^4)}} = 0.$$

(iv) $\underset{x\to\infty}{\text{Lt]}} \; x \sin \frac{1}{x} = \underset{h\to 0}{\text{Lt}} \frac{\sin h}{h} = 1$

(Banaras 1946, 1956.)

EXAMPLES IV.

1. Prove that $\underset{x\to\infty}{\text{Lt}} \dfrac{x^2-2x}{x^3-3x} = 0.$

Evaluate the following limits:—

2. $\underset{x\to 1}{\text{Lt}} \dfrac{x^p-1}{x^q-1}$ (1956) 3. $\underset{x\to 0}{\text{Lt}} \dfrac{e^x-e^{-x}}{x}$

(Banaras 1951.)

4. $\underset{x\to 0}{\text{Lt}} \dfrac{p^{-x}-q^x}{x}$ 5. $\underset{x\to 0}{\text{Lt}} \dfrac{p^x-1}{q^x-1}$ 6. $\underset{x\to\infty}{\text{Lt}} \dfrac{\sqrt{(1+x)}}{x}$

7. $\underset{x\to 0}{\text{Lt}} \dfrac{lx+\dfrac{m}{x}}{nx+\dfrac{p}{x}}$ 8. $\underset{x\to\infty}{\text{Lt}} a^x \sin\dfrac{3}{a^x}$ (1955.)

9. $\underset{x\to\infty}{\text{Lt}} \dfrac{\sqrt{(2+3x+x^2)}}{x}$

10. Prove that (i) $\underset{x\to 1}{\text{Lt}} \dfrac{\log x}{x-1}=1$ (Banaras 1946, 195?.)

(ii) $\underset{x\to a}{\text{Lt}} \dfrac{x^m-a^m}{x^n-a^n}=\dfrac{m}{n}a^{m-n}$

(Banaras 1940.)

CHAPTER II

THE DIFFERENTIAL COEFFICIENT APPLICATIONS

11. The Differential Coefficient.

Let

$$y=x^2$$

be a function of x. Let us study the behaviour of this function for $x=2$. A table of values of x near the value 2 and the corresponding values of y would be instructive.

x	2·5	2·3	2·1	2·01	2·0001
y	6·25	5·29	4·41	4·0401	4·004001

At the pt. $x=2$, $y=4$. If we give a small increment ·5 to x, y is increased by 2·25 ; if the increment in x is ·3, that in y is 1·29 and so on. We denote the small increments in x and y by δx and δy respectively and prepare a corresponding table of values of δx, δy and $\dfrac{\delta y}{\delta x}$.

δx	·5	·3	·1	·01	·001
δy	2·25	1·29	·41	·0401	·004001
$\delta y/\delta x$	4·5	4·3	4·1	4·01	4·001

We see from this table that as δx, and consequently δy, get smaller and smaller, the ratio $\frac{\delta y}{\delta x}$ approaches nearer and nearer 4. This raises the presumption that when δx, and consequently δy, become indefinitely small, the limit of the ratio $\frac{\delta y}{\delta x}$ is probably 4.

Let us prepare a corresponding table for the point $x=1$.

x	1·4	1·2	1·1	1·01	1·001
y	1·96	1·44	1·21	1·0201	1·002001
δx	·4	·2	·1	·01	·001
δy	·96	·44	·21	·0201	·002001
$\delta y/\delta x$	2·4	2·2	2·1	2·01	2·001

Here too, we notice that as δx becomes smaller and smaller, $\frac{\delta y}{\delta x}$ approaches nearer and nearer the value 2.

Has then the ratio $\frac{\delta y}{\delta x}$ a definite limiting value for every value of x ?

Again, in the equation $y=x^2$,
let us give a small increment δx to x and let the resulting increment in y be denoted by δy. Then

$$y+\delta y=(x+\delta x)^2.$$

$$\therefore \quad \delta y=(x+\delta x)^2-x^2=\delta x(2x+\delta x).$$

$$\therefore \quad \frac{\delta y}{\delta x}=2x+\delta x$$

$$\therefore \quad \underset{\delta x\to 0}{\text{Lt}} \frac{\delta y}{\delta x}=2x.$$

Now, this limit of $\frac{\delta y}{\delta x}$ when $\delta x\to 0$ is called the first differential coefficient of x^2 with respect to x. So that the first differential coefficient of x^2 with respect to x is $2x$. And this result agrees with our presumption from the above tables, for when $x=2$, this limit is 4 and when $x=1$, it is 2.

Generally, let $y=f(x)$.

Then $y+\delta y=f(x+\delta x)$.

$\therefore \quad \delta y=f(x+\delta x)-f(x)$.

$$\text{Hence} \underset{\delta x\to 0}{\text{Lt}} \frac{\delta y}{\delta x}=\underset{\delta x\to 0}{\text{Lt}} \frac{f(x+\delta x)-f(x)}{\delta x}.$$

And this limit is called the First Differential Coefficient of $f(x)$ with respect to x. The operation of finding this limit is called "differentiating $f(x)$".

By convention this limit is written as $\frac{dy}{dx}$. So that

$$\frac{dy}{dx}=\underset{\delta x\to 0}{\text{Lt}} \frac{\delta y}{\delta x}=\underset{\delta x\to 0}{\text{Lt}} \frac{f(x+\delta x)-f(x)}{\delta x}.$$

12. It should be distinctly understood that whereas $\frac{\delta y}{\delta x}$ is the ratio of δy to δx, $\frac{dy}{dx}$ is not a ratio but the result of finding the limit. To say that $\frac{dy}{dx}$ is "*dy* divided by *dx*" is as incorrect as to say that "cos *x*" is the product of "cos" and "*x*".

Other symbols expressing the same thing are $\frac{df(x)}{dx}$, $\frac{df}{dx}$, $f'(x), f', \dot{f}, f^x, y', \dot{y}, y_1, D_xY$.

Sometimes h is written instead of δx and $\frac{dy}{dx}$ is defined as

$$\underset{h \to 0}{\mathrm{Lt}} \frac{f(x+h)-f(x)}{h}.$$

But in the beginning the student will do well to use δx instead of h so that he may constantly bear in mind the essential connection between x and δx. We shall use them interchangeably.

Thus we see that to find the first differential coefficient, or the $\frac{\text{“}d\text{”}}{dx}$ of a function we must,

(1) increase x to $x+\delta x$,

(2) subtract the original value of the function,

(3) divide the remainder by δx, and

(4) evaluate the limit when δx tends to 0.

This will give us the desired result.

13. Solved Examples.

(1) Find $\dfrac{dy}{dx}$ when $y=\sqrt{x}$.

Here $f(x) = \sqrt{x}$,

and $f(x+\delta x)=\sqrt{(x+\delta x)}$.

$\therefore$ The differential coefficient$=\underset{\delta x\to 0}{\text{Lt}} \dfrac{\sqrt{(x+\delta x)}-\sqrt{x}}{\delta x}$

$$=\underset{\delta x\to 0}{\text{Lt}} \frac{(x+\delta x)-x}{\delta x\{\sqrt{(x+\delta x)}+\sqrt{x}\}}$$

$$=\underset{\delta x\to 0}{\text{Lt}} \frac{1}{\sqrt{(x+\delta x)}+\sqrt{x}}=\frac{1}{2\sqrt{x}}.$$

$$\therefore \frac{d}{dx}(\sqrt{x})=\frac{1}{2\sqrt{x}}.$$

(2) Find the diffi. coeff. of $2x^3-1$ for $x=2$.

Here $f(x)=2x^3-1$, $\quad f(x+h)=2(x+h)^3-1$

and $\dfrac{1}{h}\{f(x+h)-f(x)\}$

$$=\frac{1}{h}\{2(x+h)^3-1-(2x^3-1)\}$$

$$=\frac{1}{h}\{2(x^3+3x^2h+3xh^2+h^3)-1-(2x^3-1)\}$$

$$=\frac{1}{h}\{6x^2h+6xh^2+2h^3\}.$$

Hence the diff. coeff.

$$= \underset{h \to 0}{\text{Lt}} (6x^2 + 6xh + 2h^2) = 6x^2.$$

Therefore the diff. coeff. of $2x^3 - 1$ for $x=2$ is 24.

(3) If $s = \dfrac{1}{\theta^2}$, find $\dfrac{ds}{d\theta}$.

$$\frac{ds}{d\theta} = \underset{\delta\theta \to 0}{\text{Lt}} \frac{\dfrac{1}{(\theta+\delta\theta)^2} - \dfrac{1}{\theta^2}}{\delta\theta}$$

$$= -\underset{\delta\theta \to 0}{\text{Lt}} \frac{1}{\delta\theta} \cdot \frac{(\theta+\delta\theta)^2 - \theta^2}{\theta^2(\theta+\delta\theta)^2}$$

$$= -\underset{\delta\theta \to 0}{\text{Lt}} \frac{1}{\delta\theta} \cdot \frac{2\delta\theta(\theta+\delta\theta)}{\theta^2 (\theta+\delta\theta)^2}$$

$$= -\underset{\delta\theta \to 0}{\text{Lt}} \frac{2}{\theta^2(\theta+\delta\theta)} = -\frac{2}{\theta^3}.$$

(4) Find for what points of the curve $x^2+y=1$ is $\dfrac{dy}{dx} =$ tan 60° ?

We have $y = 1 - x^2$

$$\therefore \frac{dy}{dx} = -2x^*.$$

Hence in this case, $-2x = \tan 60 = \sqrt{3}$

* We leave this as an exercise to the student. We shall do the same in many of the following examples in this chapter.

$\therefore \quad x = -\dfrac{\sqrt{3}}{2}$ and $y = \frac{1}{4}$.

So, the point required is $\left(-\dfrac{\sqrt{3}}{2}, \frac{1}{4}\right)$.

EXAMPLES V.

Find $\dfrac{dy}{dx}$ for

1. $y = 2x + 3$. 2. $y = px + q$. 3. $y = \dfrac{1}{x}$.

4. $y = ax^2 + b$. 5. $y = a - \dfrac{1}{3x^3}$.

6. $y = \sqrt{(x^2 - a^2)} + b$. 7. $y = (a - bx)^2$.

8. $y = \log \sqrt{x}$. 9. If $s = at^2 + 2bt + c$, find $\dfrac{ds}{dt}$.

10. If $\theta = w^2 t^3 + w$, show that $\dfrac{d\theta}{dt} = 3w^2 t^2$.

11. Find for what value of x, is $\dfrac{dy}{dx}$ equal to (*i*) 2, (*ii*) 0, for $y = a^2 - x^2$.

12. Find the point of the curve $y^2 = 4ax$ for which $\dfrac{dy}{dx}$ is infinite.

13. Find for what points of the curve $\dfrac{x^2}{a^2} - \dfrac{y^2}{b^2} = 1$ is $\dfrac{dy}{dx}$ equal to $\dfrac{b}{a}\sqrt{2}$.

14. Differentiate from first principles—

(*a*) $\sin 2x$ (Banaras 1946, 1950.)

(*b*) e^{-x} (Banaras 1941.)

14. Geometrical Significance.

Let $y=f(x)$

be the equation of a curve AB and P a fixed point (x,y) on it.

Let Q be another point $(x+\delta x, y+\delta y)$ on the curve.

Then in Fig. (3)

$$\left.\begin{array}{l} OM=x, \\ ON=x+\delta x, \\ MN=\delta x \end{array}\right\} \text{ and } \left.\begin{array}{ll} MP=f(x) & =y \\ NQ=f(x+\delta x) & =y+\delta y \\ QR=f(x+\delta x)-(x) & =\delta y \end{array}\right\}$$

$$\text{Hence } \frac{QR}{PR}=\frac{(x+\delta x)-f(x)}{\delta x}=\frac{\delta y}{\delta x}.$$

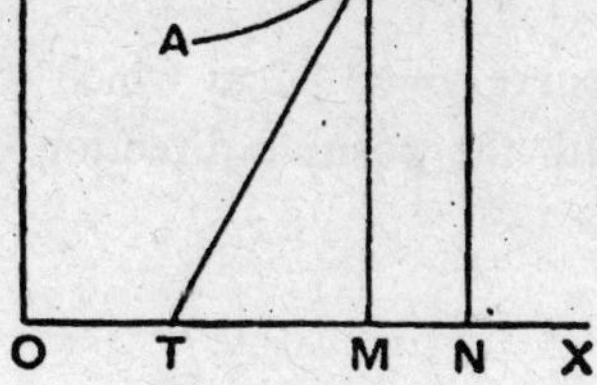

Fig 3.

Now, let Q travel along the curve towards P until i approaches indefinitely near P. In the limiting position the secant PQ becomes tht tangent to the curve at the poin P. And

$$\text{Lt}\frac{QR}{PR}t=\text{Lt} \tan RPQ=\text{Lt} \tan XTP$$

=tangent of the angle which the tangent at P to the curve makes with CX.

Again,

$$\text{Lt}\frac{QR}{PR}=\underset{\delta x\to 0}{\text{Lt}}\frac{f(x+\delta x)-f(x)}{\delta x}$$

$$= \underset{\delta x \to 0}{\text{Lt}} \frac{\delta y}{\delta x} = \frac{dy}{dx} = f'(x).$$

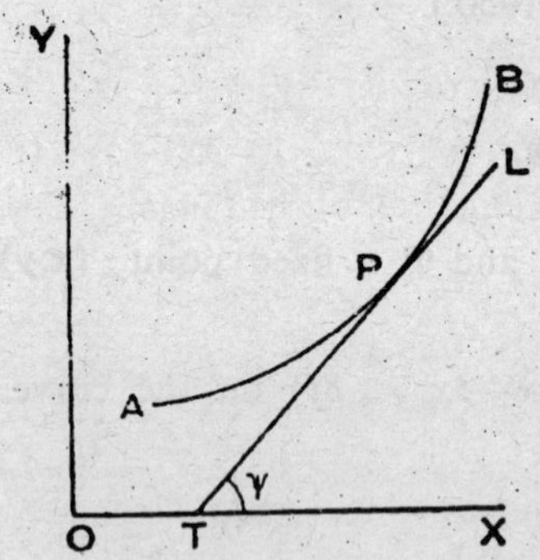

*Fig*4.

Hence the differentiate coefficient has this geometrical significance that it is equal to the tangent of the angle which the tangent to the curve $y=f(x)$ at the point (x, y) makes with the positive direction of the x-axis.

15. Now, let LPT, the tangent to the curve at P meet OX in T.

Then $\tan XTP = \frac{dy}{dx} = f'(x)$.

Hence the equation to the tangent at P to the curve $y=f(x)$

is $Y-y = \frac{dy}{dx}(X-x)$.

where X, Y are the current co-ordinates of any point on the tangent.

The angle XTP is usually denoted by ψ.

16. Solved Examples.

(1) Find the point on the curve $y=x^2+2$ at which the tangent makes an angle of 60° with the positive direction of the x-axis.

Here $y=x^2+2$,

$$\therefore \frac{dy}{dx} = 2x.$$

If $2x = \tan 60^0 = \sqrt{3}$, $x = \frac{\sqrt{3}}{2}$

$\therefore \quad y=\frac{3}{4}+2=2\frac{3}{4}.$

Hence the point is $\left(\dfrac{\sqrt{3}}{2}, 2\dfrac{3}{4}\right)$.

(2) Show that the gradient of the curve $y=3x^3+x$ at the point where $x=\frac{1}{3}$ is 2. Find the equation of the tangent there.

$y=3x^3+x$

Therefore $\dfrac{dy}{dx}=9x^2+1.$

$\therefore$ At the pt. where $x=\frac{1}{3}$, $\dfrac{dy}{dx}$ is 2. And where $x=\frac{1}{3}$, $y=\frac{4}{9}$.

Hence the equation to the tangent at the point $(\frac{1}{3}, \frac{4}{9})$ is $y-\frac{4}{9}=2(x-\frac{1}{3})$,

i.e., $18x-9y=2.$

EXAMPLES VI.

Find the equation to the tangent at the point (x, y) to the following curves :—

1. $y=\sqrt{x}+3.$
2. $y=e^x$ (Banaras 1946.)
3. $y=\cos x.$
4. $x^2y=1.$
5. $x^2-y^2=a^2.$
6. $\dfrac{x^2}{a^2}-\dfrac{y^2}{b^2}=1.$
7. (*i*) $\dfrac{x^2}{a^2}+\dfrac{y^2}{b^2}=1.$ (1956.) (*ii*) $y=\tan^{-1} x.$

(Banaras 1940.)

8. Find the point on the curve

$$x=\sqrt{3}(x^2-y+1)$$

where the tangent makes an angle of 150° with the positive irection of the axis of x. Find the equation of the tangent at the point.

9. Find the points on the curve $xy+4=0$ at which $\psi=45°$. Find the equations to the tangents at the points.

10. Find the equation of the tangent to the parabola $y^2=4x$ at the point (4, 4).

11. Show that the curves $y=x^2$ and $y=x^3$ intersect at the origin and at the point (1, 1) and that at the latter point the angle between the tangents is $\tan^{-1}\frac{1}{7}$. (Banaras 1951.)

17. Rate Measure.

We have seen in § 11 that $\frac{\delta y}{\delta x}$ denotes the ratio of the increment in y, corresponding to a small increment δx in x, to δx. If, as x increases, y increases, both δx and δy are positive and the ratio is positive. But if y decreases as x increases, δy is $-$ve while δx is $+$ve. Hence the ratio is$-$ve.

Now, let us proceed to the limit

$$\underset{\delta x\to 0}{\text{Lt}}\ \frac{\delta y}{\delta x}=\frac{dy}{dx}$$

Thus $\frac{dy}{dx}$ measures the rate at which y increases when the increment in x is infinitely small. If x and y increase together, $\frac{dy}{dx}$ is $+$ ve. If y decreases as x increases, $\frac{dy}{dx}$ is$-$ve. Thus we see that when x increases, then

(a) If y' is +ve, y increases ;
(b) If y' is −ve, y decreases.

18. Let us turn our attention once again to fig. (3). $\frac{\delta y}{\delta x}$ denotes the ratio $\frac{QR}{PR}$ or tan QPR. If both QR and PR are +ve as in the figure, the ratio is +ve. But if, for a small increment in x, there is a corresponding decrease in y, QR is −ve, while PR ı +ve. This is illustrated in fig. (5) where QN, the final value of y is less than PM, its initial value. Here one point is worth noticing : we are not concerned with the fact whether y is + ve or−ve, but only with the fact whether δy is +ve or −ve. Thus in the adjoining

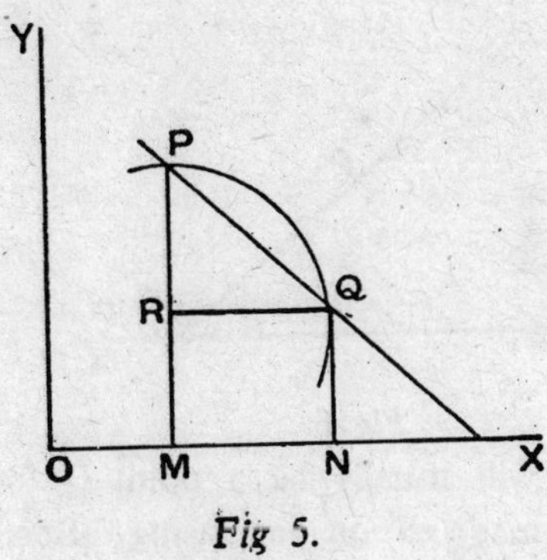

Fig 5.

figure, y remains+ve at Q but as QN, its value at Q is less than PM, its value at P, δy, the increment in y, is −ve.

19. Now, in fig. (3) let Q move upto and coincide with P. The secant PQ becomes LPT, the tangent at

P and the angle QPR becomes the angle ψ. (See fig. 4) We see that ψ is an acute angle and hence its tangent is +ve. So that in fig. (4) $\frac{dy}{dx}$ is +ve.

But when Q moves upto and coincides with P, fig. (5) assumes the form given in fig. (6).

Here we see tha ψ is an obtuse angle and consequently its tangent $\frac{dy}{dx}$ is −ve.

Let us study the changes in ψ more closely in fig. (7). At P, ψ is acute. At R it is obtuse. But between these

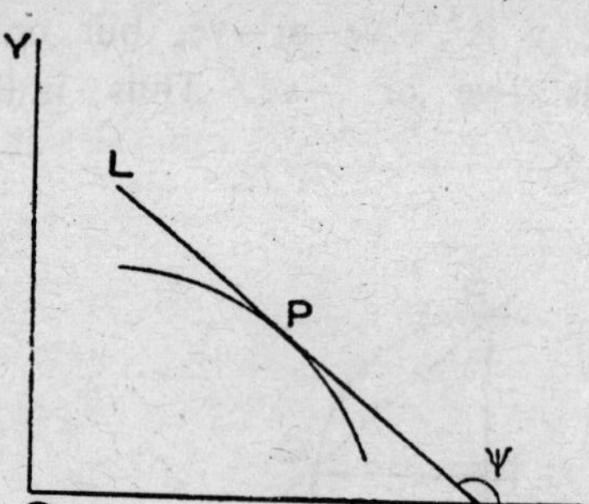

Fig 6.

two points there will usually be a point Q for which ψ is a right angle. ψ may go on increasing after R until at the point S it becomes a straight angle. On the other hand if we follow the curve beyond $SRQP$, there might be a point N where ψ is 0.

Thus, at the pt. N, $\frac{dy}{dx}$ is 0 and form this point it begins to increase. It goes on increasing until at Q, where the tangent to the curve is perpendicular to OX, it becomes ∞. From immediately before Q to immediately after Q it jumps from $+\infty$ to $-\infty$ and then goes on increasing from $-\infty$ until at the pt. S, where the tangent to the curve is parallel to OX, it is again 0.

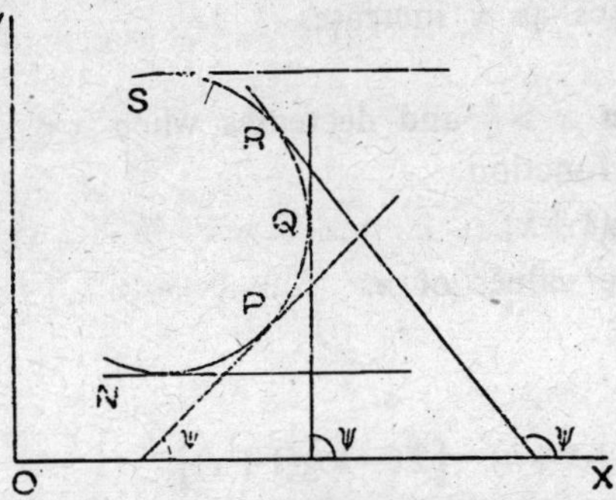

Fig. 7

Note 1.—We have seen that $f'(x)$ measures the degree of rapidity of the increment of the function $f(x)$. It differs not only from one function to another, but also for the same function according to the value of x. Thus, in fig. (7) on the same curve $PQRS$, it is +ve at P and —ve at R.

Note 2.—The words *increase* and *decrease* in reference to a function mean the algebraic, and not numerical increase or decrease. Thus we have said that in fig. (7) $\frac{dy}{dx}$ *increases* from $-\infty$ to 0 from Q to S, though the numerical value of $\frac{dy}{dx}$ has decreased. If the temperature of a body changes from -20° to -10° we say that it has *increased* from -20° to -10°.

20. Solved Examples.

(1) For what values of x is the function $y=x^2-3x+2$ increasing ? For what values decreasing ?

Here $\dfrac{dy}{dx}=2x-3.$

If $\dfrac{dy}{dx}>0$, y increases as x increases.

If $\dfrac{dy}{dx}<0$, y decreases as x increases.

$\therefore$ y increases when $x>\frac{3}{2}$ and decreases when $x<\frac{3}{2}$.

(2) Show that the function

$$f(x)=2x-\log(1+x)$$

is positive for all positive values of x.

Here $f(0)=0$

And $f'(x)$

$$=\underset{h\to 0}{\text{Lt}}\frac{2x+2h-\log(1+x+h)-\{2x-\log(1+x)\}}{h}$$

$$=\underset{h\to 0}{\text{Lt}}\frac{1}{h}\left\{2h-\log\frac{1+x+h}{1+x}\right\}$$

$$=\underset{h\to 0}{\text{Lt}}\left\{2-\frac{1}{h}\log\left(1+\frac{h}{1+x}\right)\right\}$$

$$=\underset{h\to 0}{\text{Lt}}\left[2-\frac{1}{h}\left\{\frac{h}{1+x}-\frac{h^2}{2(1+x)^2}+\ldots\right\}\right]$$

$$=2-\frac{1}{1+x}=\frac{2x+1}{1+x}.$$

So that $f'(x)$ is postitive for all positive values of x. Therefore as x increases from 0 to ∞, $f(x)$ is always increasing. Hence, since $f(0)=0$ and $f(x)$ is always increasing, it follows that $f(x)$ is positive for all positive values of x*.

(3) If A be the area of a circle of radius r, show that the circumference is $\frac{dA}{dr}$.

Here $A=\pi r^2$.

$$\therefore \frac{dA}{dr} = \underset{h \to 0}{\text{Lt}} \frac{\pi(r+h)^2-\pi r^2}{h}$$

$$= \underset{h \to 0}{\text{Lt}} \frac{2\pi rh+\pi h^2}{h}$$

$$= \pi \underset{h \to 0}{\text{Lt}} (2r+h) = 2\pi r = \text{circumference.}$$

This means that if by some process the circle goes on slowly increasing, the increment in the area is $2\pi r$ times the increment in the radius. Or, the increment in area is the area of a rectangle one of whose sides is the present circumference and the other is the small increment in the radius of the circle.

EXAMPLES VII.

1. Determine at what points of the following curves the tangent is horizontal (*i.e.*, parallel to the x-axis).

(1) $y=x^3-3x^2+2$.

(2) $y=2x^2+4x-3$.

2. Determine at what points of the following curves the tangent is vertical :

(1) $y=\sqrt{(x+2)}$

---

*It has been assumed that $f(x)$ is continuous.

(2) $y=\sqrt{(x^2-a^2)}$

3. For what values of x are the following functions increasing ?

(1) $y=x^2-10x+8$.

(2) $6y=2x^3-9x^2+12x+a$.

4. Find at what points of the circle $x^2+y^2=a^2$ the tangent cuts off equal intercepts from the axes.

(We should have $\tan \psi=\pm 1$)

5. Find where the ordinate of the curve $y=2x^2-3x$ increases at the same rate as the abscissa, and where it decreases 7 times as fast as the abscissa, increases.

6. Show that in the curve $2x+y=2\frac{1}{3}$, the ordinate decreases twice as fast as the abscissa increases.

7. The volume of a sphere is increasing at a constant rate; prove that the surface-increase varies inversely as the length of the radius.

8. Show that the function $(x-1)\, e^x+1$ is positive for all positive values of x.

9. Apply the principles of Calculus to determine where the tangent is parallel to the axis of x and where it is perpendicular to that axis for the ellipse.

$$\frac{x^2}{a^2}+\frac{y^2}{b^2}=1. \qquad \text{(Banaras 1952)}$$

10. On the curve $5cy=x^2+2ax$ find the point at which the tangent is parallel to the axis of x.

11. Write down the equation of the tangent to the curve $y=e^x$ at the point where the curve cuts the y-axis.

21. Repeated Differentiation.

We have seen that $\dfrac{dy}{dx}$ is itself a function of x.

We may proceed again to differentiate this function and obtain $\dfrac{d}{dx}\left(\dfrac{dy}{dx}\right)$. This is called the second differential coefficient or the second derivative of y. It is denoted by the following symbols

$$\frac{d^2y}{dx^2}, D_x^2y, y'', y_2, f''(x), \frac{d^2}{dx^2}f(x).$$

In the same way we may go on differentiating and obtaining the third, fourth ... nth differential coefficients. These are written as

$$\frac{d^3y}{dx^3}, \frac{d^4y}{dx^4}, \ldots\ldots, \frac{d^ny}{dx^n}$$

22. Geometrical Significance.

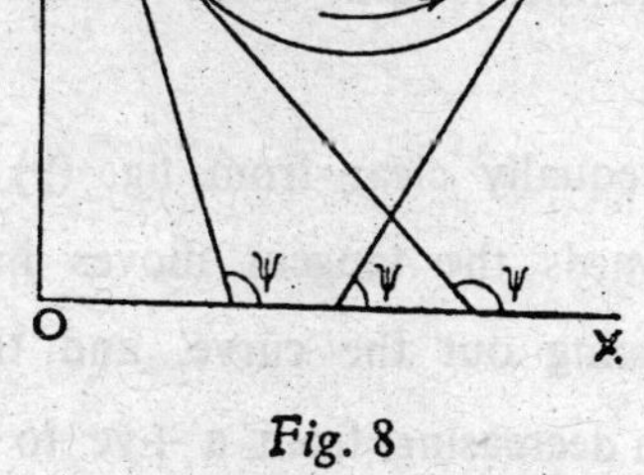

Fig. 8

We have seen that $\tan\psi = \dfrac{dy}{dx}$

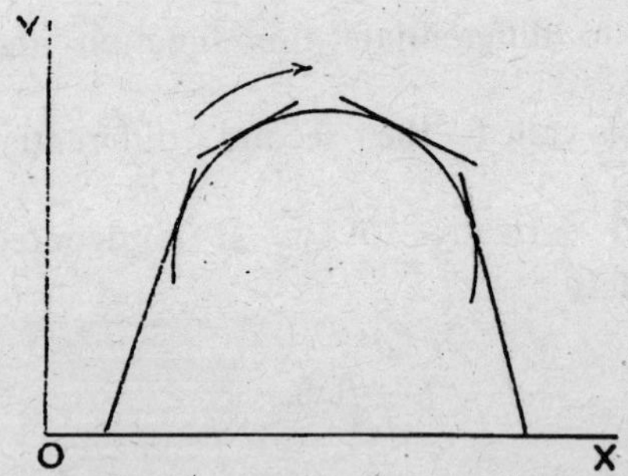

Fig. 9

Let $y=f(x)$ be a curve which is concave upwards, *i.e.*, concave as seen by a person stationed above the curve. Consider the tangent at a variable point P. Let us imagine the tangent to be moving round and thus tracing out the curve. At P, ψ is obtuse; hence $\tan\psi$ is $-$ve. As we move towards Q and R, $\tan\psi$, *i.e.*, $\dfrac{dy}{dx}$ goes on increasing algebraically, from a $-$ve quantity to 0 and then to a $+$ve quantity, as ψ changes from an obtuse to an acute angle. So that, in a curve concave upwards, the slope of the tangent, *i.e.*, $\dfrac{dy}{dx}$ goes on increasing as the tangent turns round in the counter-clockwise sense.

It will be equally clear from fig. (9) that in a curve concave downwards the tangent moves in the clockwise direction in tracing out the curve, and the slope of the tangent goes on decreasing from a $+$ve to a $-$ve quantity.

Hence our conclusion is that

in fig. (8) as x increases, $\dfrac{dy}{dx}$ increases;

in fig. (9) as x increases, $\dfrac{dy}{dx}$ decreases.

Now, we have seen that as x increases,

y increases if $\dfrac{dy}{dx} > 0$;

y decreases if $\dfrac{dy}{dx} < 0$.

But in this case we are considering the function $\dfrac{dy}{dx}$ in place of y. Hence we must have:

As x increases,

in fig. (8) $\dfrac{d}{dx}\left(\dfrac{dy}{dx}\right)$ i.e., $\dfrac{d^2y}{dx^2} > 0$:

in fig. (9) $\dfrac{d}{dx}\left(\dfrac{dy}{dx}\right)$ i.e., $\dfrac{d^2y}{dx^2} < 0$.

That is to say, the curve $y=f(x)$;
is concave upwards if $f''(x) > 0$;
is concave downwards if $f''(x) < 0$.

23. Solved Example.

In what intervals is the curve $2y = x^3 - 6x^2 + 2$
(1) concave upwards (2) concave downwards?

We have $y=\frac{1}{2}x^3-3x^2+1$

$$y_1=\tfrac{1}{2}(3x^2-12x)$$

and $y_2=3(x-2)$.

Hence the curve is

concave upwards when $x>2$;

concave downwards when $x<2$.

24. We added a few miscellaneous examples.

(1) A small error δr is made in measuring the radius r of a sphere. Find the corresponding error in the computed volume of the sphere. If the radius is 10 ins. show that the approximate value of the error made in the volume is 80π sq. ins. if the error in the radius be ·2 in.

Let V be the volume of the sphere, and δV the error in V due to the error in the radius. Then

$$V=\tfrac{4}{3}\pi r^3,$$

$$V+\delta V=\tfrac{4}{3}\pi(r+\delta r)^3.$$

$$\therefore\ \delta V=\tfrac{4}{3}\pi\left\{(r+\delta r)^3-r^3\right\}$$
$$=\tfrac{4}{3}\pi\left\{3r^2(\delta r)+3r(\delta r)^2+(\delta r)^3\right\}.$$

$$\therefore\ \frac{\delta V}{\delta r}=4\pi r^2+4\pi r(\delta r)+\tfrac{4}{3}\pi(\delta r)^2.$$

We are concerned only with the ratio $\dfrac{\delta V}{\delta r}$. Hence, neglecting δr and $(\delta r)^2$ as δr is a small quantity, we have

$$\frac{\delta V}{\delta r}=4\pi r^2 \textit{ i.e., } \delta V=4\pi r^2\delta r$$

approximately.

Now, $r=10$ ins. and $\delta r=\cdot 2$ in.

$\therefore\ \delta V=4\pi(10)^2(\cdot 2)$ sq. ins.

$=80\pi$ sq. ins.

(2) A ladder 18 ft. long is leaning against a vertical wall. The foot of the ladder is moved away from the wall, at a uniform rate of 6 ins. per sec. Find the rate at which the top of the ladder is descending on the wall, when the foot is 9 ft. from the wall.

Let AB be the initial position of the ladder and $A'B'$ its position after a sec.

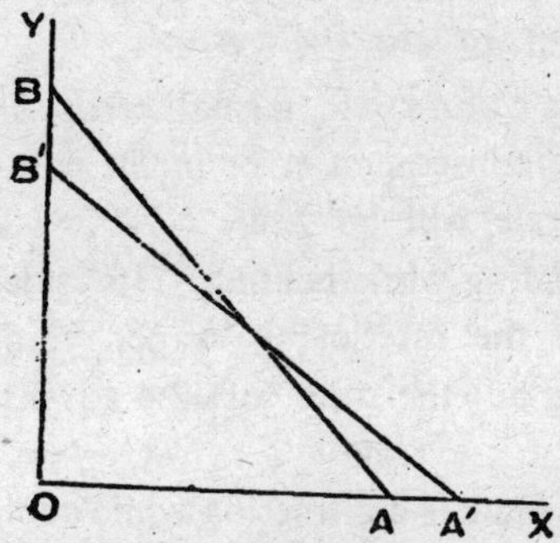

Fig. 10

Let $OA=a$, $OB=b$, $AA'=\delta a$, $B'B=\delta b$.

Let c be the length of the ladder. Then

$$c^2=a^2+b^2;$$

and $c^2=(a+\delta a)^2+(b-\delta b)^2$

$\therefore\ 0=2a\delta a+(\delta a)^2-2b\delta b+(\delta b)^2$.

Therefore, neglecting squares of δa and δb we have

$$\delta b=\frac{a}{b}\delta a.$$

Now, $a=9$ ft., $AB=18$ ft.

Therefore $b=9\sqrt{3}$ ft.

Also $\delta a=6$ ins.

$$\therefore\ \delta b=\frac{9}{9\sqrt{3}}6'' \text{ per sec.}$$

$=2\sqrt{3}$ in. per sec.

EXAMPLES VIII.

1. For what values of x are the curves

(*i*) $6y=x^3-3x^2+12$

(*ii*) $12y-x^4-8x^3+18x^2$

(*a*) concave upwards (*b*) concave downwards?

2. Show that the diff. coeff. of x^3+3 is $3x^2$.

3. In measuring the radius r of a circle, a small error δr has been made. Show that the consequent error in the computed circumference of the circle will be $2\pi\delta r$.

4. A square plate is expanding while heating. Its side, when 12 ins., is increasing at the rate of ·1 in. per min. Show that the area is increasing at the rate of 2·4 sq. ins. per min.

5. The area of a circular plate is contracting while cooling. When the radius is 6 ins. it is diminishing at the rate of ·03 in. per sec. Show that the area is decreasing at the rate of $\cdot 36\pi$ sq. in. per sec. at the time.

6. In measuring the radius r of a sphere a small error δr has been made. Show that the consequent error in the computed surface of the sphere is $8\pi r\delta r$.

If the radius is 2·5 ins. and the error in measuring it ·05 in. show that the percentage error in the surface is 4.

7. A cone has a height h ins. and a radius r ins. There is a possible small error δr in r. Find approximately the possible error in the computed volume.

8. Two lines OA and OB at right angles are measured, their lengths being given as 27 and 36 ins. respectively. If a possible error of 1 in. has to be allowed for in the measurement of OA, what is the amount of the possible error in the length of AB as calculated from the measurements?

9. The length l of a bar at temperature t^0 is given by the relation

$$l=at^2+2bt+2.$$

When t was 0, l was 2. Find the rate of increment of the bar at temperature t^0. What is the increase in length corresponding to a small increase in temperature ?

25. **Application to Dynamics: Velocity.**—When we say that a train is moving at the rate of 22 ft. per sec., we imply that the space described in any interval depends on the length of the interval. In other words, space is a function of time. For instance, in the example chosen,

$$s=22t,$$

where s is measured in ft. and t in secs. For another instance let us study the motion of a particle which is increasing its velocity at every instant—as is the case of a body falling to the ground.

Let the law of motion of the particle be given by the formula

$$s=8t^2.$$

After 1 sec. from the start, the space described is

$s=8.$

After $\frac{1}{10}$ sec. more, *i.e*, after $1\frac{1}{10}$ secs. from the start,

$s'^{*}=8({}_{1}{}^{1})^2={}^{242}.$

Hence the average velocity during the $\frac{1}{10}$th of a sec. under consideration is

---

*Here the dash (′) does not denote differentiation.

$$\frac{s'-s}{\frac{1}{10}}=\frac{\frac{242}{25}-8}{\frac{1}{10}}=16\tfrac{4}{5} \text{ ft. per sec.}$$

But during the $\frac{1}{10}$th of a sec. the velocity will not be uniform. In the beginning of this interval it will be slightly less, and towards the end, slightly more than this average velocity. Hence, to find a closer approximation let us consider the $\frac{1}{100}$th of a sec. immediately following the first second, instead of $\frac{1}{10}$th of a sec.

$$s''=8(\tfrac{101}{100})^2=\tfrac{10201}{1250}.$$

Therefore, the average velocity during this $\frac{1}{100}$th of a sec. will be

$$\frac{s''-s}{\frac{1}{100}}=\frac{\frac{10201}{1250}-8}{\frac{1}{100}}=16\tfrac{2}{25} \text{ ft. per sec.}$$

But during this $\frac{1}{100}$th of a sec. too the velocity will not be uniform. In the beginning of this interval it will be slightly less and in the end slightly more than this average velocity. To get a still closer approximation we might consider $\frac{1}{1000}$th of a sec. instead of $\frac{1}{100}$th. But can we not get rid of the cumbersome process of getting closer and closer approximations by considering smaller and smaller intervals ? Differential Calculus affords the answer.

Let δt be a very small interval of time after any interval of time t from the start. Let δs be the distance traversed in the small time δt. Then we have

$$s=8t^2,$$

$$s+\delta s=8(t+\delta t)^2.$$

$$\therefore \delta s=8\{(t+\delta t)^2-t^2)\}=16t\delta t+8(\delta t)^2.$$

Therefore, the average velocity during the small interval δt is

$$\frac{\delta s}{t}=16t+8\delta t.$$

Let now the interval δt be made infinitely small. Then, proceeding to the limit, we have,

$$\text{the average velocity}=\underset{\delta t\to 0}{\text{Lt}}\ \frac{\delta s}{\delta t}=16t.$$

And, generally speaking, let the law of motion be

$$s=f(t),$$

so that the space described, in an interval $t+\delta t$ from the start, is,

$$s+\delta s=f(t+\delta t).$$

Then $\dfrac{\delta s}{\delta t}=\dfrac{f(t+\delta t)-f(t)}{\delta t}.$

$$\therefore\ \text{Average velocity}=\underset{\delta t\to 0}{\text{Lt}}\ \frac{\delta s}{\delta t}$$

$$=\underset{\delta t\to 0}{\text{Lt}}\frac{f(t+\delta t)-f(t)}{\delta t}=f'(t).$$

Hence the average velocity at any instant is given by the diff. coeff. of space with respect to time, *i.e.*, by $\dfrac{ds}{dt}$.

26. Solved Example.

The height of a stone thrown vertically upwards is given by the formula,

$$s=21t-7t^2.$$

Find (a) its velocity at the end of 1 sec. (b) how high it will rise.

(a) We have, velocity

$$\frac{ds}{dt}=21-14t.$$

Putting $t=1$, the velocity after 1 sec. is given by

$$\frac{ds}{dt}=21-14=7 \text{ ft. per sec.}$$

(b) The stone will go on rising till its velocity is 0. Hence, putting $\frac{ds}{dt}=0$, we see that the stone will come to rest in $1\frac{1}{2}$ secs.

And the distance traversed in $1\frac{1}{2}$ secs.

$$=21(\tfrac{3}{2})-7(\tfrac{3}{2})^2=15\tfrac{3}{4} \text{ ft.}$$

27. It appears now that $\frac{ds}{dt}$ means the rate of increase of s in point of time. Let now the current co-ordinates of a moving particle be x and y at the instant under consideration. Then $\frac{dx}{dt}$, $\frac{dy}{dt}$ mean the rates of change of x and y, *i.e.*, the components of the velocity $\frac{ds}{dt}$ resolved parallel to the axes.

If δx, δy be the increments in x and y in the small time δt, we have

$$\frac{dy}{dx}=\text{Lt}\frac{\delta y}{\delta x}=\underset{\delta t\to 0}{\text{Lt}}\frac{\frac{\delta y}{\delta t}}{\frac{\delta x}{\delta t}}=\frac{\frac{dy}{dt}}{\frac{dx}{dt}}$$

Hence $\frac{dy}{dx}$ represents the ratio of the rate of change of y to that of x.

28. The derivate $\frac{ds}{dt}$ is itself a function of t. And just as $\frac{ds}{dt}$ means the rate of change of s with respect to t, in the same way $\frac{d}{dt}\left(\frac{ds}{dt}\right)$ or $\frac{d^2s}{dt^2}$ means the rate of change of $\frac{ds}{dt}$ with respect to t, *i.e.*, the acceleration of the velocity. If the velocity is increasing with time, it is +ve ; if it is decreasing it is −ve, and is known as 'retardation'.

29. Solved Example.

A particle moves in such a way that the space described is proportional to the square of the time of description. Prove that the velocity will vary as the time and the acceleration of the velocity will be constant.

Let $s=\lambda\ t^2$.

Then, velocity $\dfrac{ds}{dt}=2\lambda t \propto t$.

And, acceleration $\dfrac{d^2s}{dt^2}=2\lambda=\text{constant}$.

EXAMPLES IX.

1. An aeroplane travels a distance of $(5t+6t^2)$ ft. in t secs. What is its velocity when it has moved for 3 mins. ?

2. A stone is ascending in the air, its motion being governed by the formula,

$$s=48t-3t^2.$$

Find (1) its velocity at the end of 2 secs,
(2) how long it will go on rising,
(3) the maximum height it reaches.

3. An aeroplane moves a distance of $(3t^2+2t)$ ft. in t secs. Find its velocity when it has flown for 5 mins.

4. A particle moves so that the space it describes varies as the cube of the time. Show that the velocity at any instant is proportional to the square of the time and the acceleration varies as the time.

5. The velocity of an airship moving horizontally with the engines shut off was observed at successive instants of time. When the reciprocal of the velocity was plotted against the time the graph was found to be a straight line. Prove that the retardation varied as the square of the velocity.

6. If $s=ut-\frac{1}{2}ft^2$ find the values of the velocity and acceleration at the time t.

7. A particle moves, its motion being governed by the formula

$$s \propto \cos \mu t,$$

where μ is a constant. Show that the retardation is proportional to the distance of the particle measured along its path from a fixed position.

8. A point moves in a fixed straight path so that

$$s=\sqrt{t}\ ;$$

show that the acceleration is negative and that it varies as the cube of the velocity. (Banaras 1939)

9. A particle is going up in the air and its motion is governed by the condition $s=60t-5t^2$. Find by the method of calculus—

(a) its velocity when $t=3$;

(b) the maximum height reached ;

(c) the time taken to reach the maximum height.

(Banaras 1944)

10. An aeroplane travels s miles in t hrs. from its start, where

$$s=200t+7t^2\ ;$$

find the velocity of the aeroplane at the end of 3 hrs.

(Banaras 1945, 1956)

CHAPTER III

STANDARD FORMS

30. In this chapter we differentiate some of the elementary Standard Forms.

31. $\mathbf{x^n}$.

Let $u = f(x) = x^n$

Then $f(x+\delta x) = (x+\delta x)^n$

$$\therefore \frac{du}{dx} = \underset{\delta x \to 0}{\text{Lt}} \frac{(x+\delta x)^n - x^n}{\delta x}$$

$$= \underset{\delta x \to 0}{\text{Lt}}\ x^n \frac{\left(1+\dfrac{\delta x}{x}\right)^n - 1}{\delta x}$$

Since δx is to be ultimately 0, we may consider $\dfrac{\delta x}{x}$ to be less than unity. Hence, applying the Binomial Theorem we have

$$\frac{du}{dx} = \underset{\delta x \to 0}{\text{Lt}} \frac{x^n}{\delta x} \cdot \left\{ n\frac{\delta x}{x} + \frac{n(n-1)}{2!} \cdot \frac{(\delta x)^2}{x^2} + \frac{n(n-1)(n-2)}{3!} \cdot \frac{(\delta x)^3}{x^3} + \dots \right\}$$

$$= \underset{\delta x \to 0}{\text{Lt}}\ nx^{n-1} \left\{ 1 + \frac{\delta x}{x} \times \text{a convergent series.} \right\}$$

$$= nx^{n-1}$$

So, $\frac{d}{dx}(x^n)=nx^{n-1}$

32. a^x.

Let $u=f(x)=a^x$.

Then $f(x+h)=a^{x+h}$

$$\therefore \frac{du}{dx}=\underset{h\to 0}{\text{Lt}}\frac{a^{x+h}-a^x}{h}=a^x\underset{h\to 0}{\text{Lt}}\frac{a^h-1}{h}$$

$$=a^x\log_e a$$

So, $\frac{d}{dx}(a^a)=a^x \log_e a$.

Cor. If $a=e$, $u=e^x$

and $\frac{du}{dx}=e^x \log_e e=e^x$.

33. $\log_a{}^x$.

Let $u=f(x)=\log_a x$.

Then $f(x+h)=\log_a(x+h)$.

$$\therefore \frac{du}{dx}=\underset{h\to 0}{\text{Lt}}\frac{\log_a(x+h)-\log_a x.}{h}$$

$$=\underset{h\to 0}{\text{Lt}}\frac{1}{h}\log_a\left(1+\frac{h}{x}\right)$$

Let $\frac{x}{h}=t$, so that $t\to\infty$, when $h\to 0$.

$$\text{Then } \frac{du}{dx}=\underset{t\to\infty}{\text{Lt}}\frac{t}{x}\text{o}\,g_a\left(1+\frac{1}{t}\right)$$

$$=\underset{\to\infty}{\text{Lt}}\frac{1}{x}\log_a\left(1+\frac{1}{t}\right)^t=\frac{1}{x}\log_a e \;(\S\ 8).$$

So, $\dfrac{d}{dx}(\log_a x)=\dfrac{1}{x}\log_a e.$

Cor. If $a=e$, $u=\log_e x$ and $\dfrac{du}{dx}=\dfrac{1}{x}\log_e e=\dfrac{1}{x}$

So, $\dfrac{d}{dx}(\log x)=\dfrac{1}{x}.$

EXAMPLES X.

1. Write down the differential coefficients of

x^2, x^3, x^9, $\sqrt{x}$, $\dfrac{1}{\sqrt{x}}$, $\dfrac{1}{x^3}$, $x^{-3/4}$ $\dfrac{1}{\sqrt[3]{x^2}}$

Differentiate from first principles

2. (1) $\log_b bx$ (2) $a \log_b bx$
3. (1) e^{ax} (2) $b\, e^{ax}$
   (3) e^{-x} (Banaras 1941).

Write down the differential coefficients of

4. 2^x, 3^x, 2^{2x}, 3^{5x}, $\left(\frac{2}{3}\right)^x$.
5. $\log_2 x$ $\log_{10} x$, $\log_e x$.

34. Sin x.

If $f(x)=\sin x$,

$f(x+h)=\sin(x+h).$

Therefore, $f'(x)=\underset{h\to 0}{\mathrm{Lt}}\dfrac{\sin(x+h)-\sin x}{h}$

$=\underset{h\to 0}{\mathrm{Lt}}\dfrac{2}{h}\cos\left(x+\dfrac{h}{2}\right)\sin\dfrac{h}{2}$

$$= \underset{h \to 0}{\text{Lt}} \left\{ \cos\left(x + \frac{h}{2}\right) \frac{\sin\frac{h}{2}}{\frac{h}{2}} \right\}$$

But $\underset{h \to 0}{\text{Lt}} \dfrac{\sin\frac{h}{2}}{\frac{h}{2}} = \underset{t \to 0}{\text{Lt}} \dfrac{\sin t}{t} = 1.$

Hence $f'(x) = \underset{h \to 0}{\text{Lt}} \cos\left(x + \dfrac{h}{2}\right) = \cos x$

i.e., $\dfrac{d}{dx}(\sin x) = \cos x.$

35. Cos x.

If $f(x) = \cos x$,

$f(x+h) = \cos(x+h)$.

Therefore, $f'(x) = \underset{h \to 0}{\text{Lt}} \dfrac{\cos(x+h) - \cos x}{h}$

$$= \underset{h \to 0}{\text{Lt}} \left\{ -\frac{2}{h} \sin\left(x + \frac{h}{2}\right) \sin\frac{h}{2} \right\}$$

$$= -\underset{h \to 0}{\text{Lt}} \left\{ \cos\left(x + \frac{h}{2}\right) \frac{\sin\frac{h}{2}}{\frac{h}{2}} \right\}$$

$= -\sin x$

i.e., $\frac{d}{dx}(\cos x) = -\sin x.$

36. Tan x.

If $f(x) = \tan x$,

$$f'(x) = \underset{h\to 0}{\text{Lt}} \frac{\tan(x+h) - \tan x}{h}$$

$$= \underset{h\to 0}{\text{Lt}} \frac{1}{h}\left\{\frac{\sin(x+h)}{\cos(x+h)} - \frac{\sin x}{\cos x}\right\}$$

$$= \underset{h\to 0}{\text{Lt}} \frac{\sin(x+h)\cos x - \sin x\cos(x+h)}{h\cos(x+h)\cos x}$$

$$= \underset{h\to 0}{\text{Lt}} \frac{\sin h}{h\cos(x+h)\cos x} = \frac{1}{\cos^2 x}.$$

Hence $\frac{d}{dx}(\tan x) = \sec^2 x.$

37. **Cot x.**

Proceeding as in the last article, we shall have

$$\frac{d}{dx}(\cot x) = -\text{cosec}^2 x.$$

38. **Sec. x.**

Let $f(x) = \sec x$.

$$\text{Then } f'(x) = \underset{h\to 0}{\text{Lt}} \frac{\sec(x+h) - \sec x}{h}$$

$$= \underset{h\to 0}{\text{Lt}} \frac{1}{h}\left\{\frac{1}{\cos(x+h)} - \frac{1}{\cos x}\right\}$$

$$= \underset{h\to 0}{\text{Lt}} \frac{\cos x - \cos(x+h)}{h \cos(x+h) \cos x}$$

$$= \underset{h\to 0}{\text{Lt}} \frac{2 \sin\frac{h}{2} \sin\left(x+\frac{h}{2}\right)}{h \cos(x+h) \cos x}$$

$$= \underset{h\to 0}{\text{Lt}} \left\{ \frac{\sin\frac{h}{2} \sin\left(x+\frac{h}{2}\right)}{\frac{h}{2} \cos(x+h) \cos x} \right\}$$

$$= \frac{\sin x}{\cos^2 x}$$

Hence $\frac{d}{dx}(\sec x) = \frac{\sin x}{\cos^2 x} = \sec x \tan x.$

39. Cosec x.

Proceeding as above, we shall have

$$\frac{d}{dx}(\text{cosec } x) = -\frac{\cos x}{\sin^2 x} = -\text{cosec } x \cot x.$$

40. Vers x.

If $f(x) = \text{vers } x$,

$$f'(x) = \underset{h\to 0}{\text{Lt}} \frac{\text{vers}(x+h) - \text{vers } x}{h}$$

$$= \underset{h\to 0}{\text{Lt}} \frac{1}{h}[\{1-\cos(x+h)\} - \{1-\cos x\}]$$

$$=-\underset{h\to 0}{\text{Lt}}\ \frac{\cos(x+h)-\cos x}{h}$$

$$=-\frac{d}{dx}(\cos x)$$

$$=\sin x. \qquad (\S\ 35)$$

Hence $\dfrac{d}{dx}(\text{vers } x)=\sin x.$

41. Covers x.

Proceeding as above we shall find that

$$\frac{d}{dx}(\text{covers } x)=-\cos x$$

The Inverse Circular Functions.

42. Sin^{-1}x.

Let $u=\sin^{-1}x$ and $U=\sin^{-1}(x+h)$,

so that $x=\sin u$ and $x+h=\sin U$.

Then $h=\sin U-\sin u$.

Now, as $h\to 0$, $U\to u$.

Therefore, $$\frac{du}{dx}=\underset{h\to 0}{\text{Lt}}\ \frac{\sin^{-1}(x+h)-\sin^{-1}x}{h}$$

$$=\underset{U\to u}{\text{Lt}}\ \frac{U-u}{\sin U-\sin u}$$

$$= \underset{U \to u}{\text{Lt}} \frac{U-u}{\text{n}\frac{U-u}{2}\cos\frac{U+u}{2}}$$

$$= \underset{U \to u}{\text{Lt}} \frac{\frac{U-u}{2}}{\sin\frac{U-u}{2}} \cdot \frac{1}{\cos\frac{U+u}{2}}$$

$$= \frac{1}{\cos u} = \frac{1}{\sqrt{(1-\sin^2 u)}} = \frac{1}{\sqrt{(1-x^2)}}.$$

Hence $\frac{d}{dx}(\sin^{-1}x) = \frac{1}{\sqrt{(1-x^2)}}$

43. $\text{Cos}^{-1}x$.

Proceeding as above we shall find that

$$\frac{d}{dx}(\cos^{-1}x) = -\frac{1}{\sqrt{(1-x^2)}}.$$

44. $\text{Tan}^{-1}x$

Let $u = \tan^{-1}x$, and $U = \tan^{-1}(x+h)$, so that $x = \tan u$, $x+h = \tan U$.

Then $h = \tan U - \tan u$,

$$\therefore \frac{du}{dx} = \underset{h \to 0}{\text{Lt}} \frac{\tan^{-1}(x+h) - \tan^{-1}x.}{h}$$

$$= \underset{U \to u}{\text{Lt}} \frac{U-u}{\tan U - \tan u}$$

$$= \underset{U \to u}{\mathrm{Lt}} \frac{U-u}{\dfrac{\sin U}{\cos U} - \dfrac{\sin u}{\cos u}}$$

$$= \underset{U \to u}{\mathrm{Lt}} \frac{(U-u) \cos U \cos u}{\sin (U-u)}$$

$$= \underset{U \to u}{\mathrm{Lt}} \frac{(U-u) \cos U \cos u}{2 \sin \dfrac{U-u}{2} \cos \dfrac{U-u}{2}}$$

$$= \underset{U \to u}{\mathrm{Lt}} \frac{\dfrac{U-u}{2}}{\sin \dfrac{U-u}{2} \cos \dfrac{U-u}{2}} . \cos U \cos u$$

Now, $\underset{U \to u}{\mathrm{Lt}} \cos \dfrac{U-u}{2} = \underset{t \to 0}{\mathrm{Lt}} \cos t = 1.$

Hence $\dfrac{du}{dx} = \cos^2 u = \dfrac{1}{\sec^2 u} = \dfrac{1}{1+x^2}$

i.e., $\dfrac{d}{dx}(\tan^{-1} x) = \dfrac{1}{1+x^2}$

45. $\mathrm{Cot}^{-1} x$.

Proceeding as above we shall have

$$\frac{d}{dx} (\cot^{-1} x) = - \frac{1}{1+x^2}$$

46. Sec ^{-1}x.

Let $u=\sec^{-1}x$ and $U=\sec^{-1}(x+h)$.
Then $x=\sec u$ and $x+h=\sec U$.
Consequently, $h=\sec U-\sec u$.

$$\text{Therefore, } \frac{du}{dx}=\underset{h\to 0}{\text{Lt}}\frac{\sec^{-1}(x+h)-\sec^{-1}x}{h}$$

$$=\underset{U\to u}{\text{Lt}}\frac{U-u}{\sec U-\sec u}$$

$$=\underset{U\to u}{\text{Lt}}\frac{U-u}{\dfrac{1}{\cos U}-\dfrac{1}{\cos u}}$$

$$=\underset{U\to u}{\text{Lt}}\frac{(U-u)\cos U\cos u}{\cos u-\cos U}$$

$$=\underset{U\to u}{\text{Lt}}\frac{(U-u)\cos U\cos u}{2\sin\dfrac{U+u}{2}\sin\dfrac{U-u}{2}}$$

$$=\underset{U\to u}{\text{Lt}}\frac{\dfrac{U-u}{2}}{\sin\dfrac{U-u}{2}}\cdot\frac{\cos U\cos u}{\sin\dfrac{U+u}{2}}$$

$$=\frac{\cos^2 u}{\sin u}=\frac{1}{x\sqrt{(x^2-1)}}$$

Hence $\frac{d}{dx}(\sec^{-1}x) = \frac{1}{x\sqrt{(x^2-1)}}$

47. $\text{Cosec}^{-1}x$

We can easily show that

$$\frac{d}{dx}\operatorname{cosec}^{-1}x = -\frac{1}{x\sqrt{(x^2-1)}}$$

48. $\text{Vers}^{-1}x.$

Let $\text{vers}^{-1}x=u$ and $\text{vers}^{-1}(x+h)=U$, so that $x=\text{vers } u$ and $x+h=\text{vers } U$.

Hence $h=\text{vers } U-\text{vers } u.$

$$\therefore \frac{du}{dx}=\underset{h\to 0}{\text{Lt}}\frac{\text{vers}^{-1}(x+h)-\text{vers}^{-1}x}{h}$$

$$=\underset{U\to u}{\text{Lt}}\frac{U-u}{\text{vers } U-\text{vers } u}$$

$$=\underset{U\to u}{\text{Lt}}\frac{U-u}{(1-\cos U)-(1-\cos u)}$$

$$=\underset{U\to u}{\text{Lt}}\frac{U-u}{\cos u-\cos U}$$

$$=\underset{U\to u}{\text{Lt}}\frac{U-u}{2\sin\frac{U-u}{2}\sin\frac{U+u}{2}}$$

$$=\underset{U\to u}{\text{Lt}}\frac{\frac{U-u}{2}}{\sin\frac{U-u}{2}}\cdot\frac{1}{\sin\frac{U+u}{2}}$$

$$=\frac{1}{\sin u}=\frac{1}{\sqrt{(1-\cos^2 u)}}$$

But $x=\text{vers } u=1-\cos u$

i.e., $\cos u=1-x$

Hence $\frac{du}{dx}=\frac{1}{\sqrt{\{1-(1-x)^2\}}}=\frac{1}{\sqrt{(2x-x^2)}}$

i.e., $\frac{d}{dx}(\text{vers}^{-1}x)=\frac{1}{\sqrt{(2x-x^2)}}$

49. Covers^{-1}x.

$$\frac{d}{dx}(\text{covers}^{-1}x)=-\frac{1}{\sqrt{(2x-x^2)}}$$

50. Recapitulation of the results.

$f(x)=x^n$,	$f'(x)=nx^{n-1}$.
$f(x)=a^x$,	$f'(x)=a^x \log_e a$.
$f(x)=e^x$,	$f'(x)=e^x$
$f(x)=\log_a x$,	$f'(x)=\frac{1}{x}\log_a e$
$f(x)=\log_e x$	$f'(x)=\frac{1}{x}$
$f(x)=\sin x$,	$'(x)=\cos x$.
$f(x)=\cos x$,	$f'(x)=-\sin x$
$f(x)=\tan x$,	$f'(x)=\sec^2 x$.
$f(x)=\cot x$,	$f'(x)=-\text{cosec}^2 x$.
$f(x)=\text{cosec } x$,	$f'(x)=-\text{cosec } x \cot x$.
$f(x)=\text{vers } x$,	$f'(x)=\sin x$.

$f(x)=\text{covers } x,\qquad f'(x)=-\cos x.$

$$f(x)=\sin^{-1}x,\qquad f'(x)=\frac{1}{\sqrt{(1-x^2)}}$$

$$f(x)=\cos^{-1}x,\qquad f'(x)=-\frac{1}{\sqrt{(1-x^2)}}$$

$$f(x)=\tan^{-1}x,\qquad f'(x)=\frac{1}{1+x^2}$$

$$f(x)=\cot^{-1}x\qquad f'(x)=-\frac{1}{1+x^2}$$

$$f(x)=\sec^{-1}x,\qquad f'(x)=+\frac{1}{x\sqrt{(x^2-1)}}$$

$$f(x)=\text{cosec}^{-1}x,\qquad f'(x)=-\frac{1}{x\sqrt{(x^2-1)}}$$

$$f(x)=\text{vers}^{-1}x,\qquad f'(x)=\frac{1}{\sqrt{(2x-x^2)}}$$

$$f(x)=\text{covers}^{-1}x,\qquad f'(x)=-\frac{1}{\sqrt{(2x-x^2)}}$$

51. We add a few solved examples.

(1) Differentiate $\sin^2x$ from first principles.

Let $f(x)=\sin^2x$.

Then $$f'(x)=\underset{h\to0}{\text{Lt}}\frac{\sin^2(x+h)-\sin^2x}{h}$$

$$=\underset{h\to 0}{\text{Lt}}\frac{1}{h}\{\sin(x+h)+\sin x\}\{\sin(x+h)-\sin x\}$$

$$=\underset{h\to 0}{\text{Lt}}\ \frac{1}{h}.\ 2\sin\left(x+\frac{h}{2}\right)$$

$$\times\cos\frac{h}{2}.\ 2\cos\left(x+\frac{h}{2}\right)\sin\frac{h}{2}$$

$$\underset{h\to 0}{\text{Lt}}\ \frac{1}{h}\sin(2x+h)\sin h=\sin 2x.$$

(2) Differentiate $\sqrt{\cos x}$. (Banaras 1941)

If $f(x)=\sqrt{\cos x}$,

$$f'=\underset{h\to 0}{\text{Lt}}\frac{\sqrt{\{\cos(x+h)\}}-\sqrt{\cos x}}{h}$$

$$=\underset{h\to 0}{\text{Lt}}\frac{\cos(x+h)-\cos x}{h[\sqrt{\{\cos(x+h)\}}+\sqrt{\cos x}]}$$

$$=\underset{h\to 0}{\text{Lt}}\frac{-2\sin\left(x+\frac{h}{2}\right)\sin\frac{h}{2}}{h[\sqrt{\{\cos(x+h)\}}+\sqrt{\cos x}]}$$

$$=-\underset{h\to 0}{\text{Lt}}\frac{\sin\frac{h}{2}}{\frac{h}{2}}.\ \frac{\sin x+\frac{h}{2}}{\sqrt{\{\cos(x+h)\}}+\sqrt{\cos x}}$$

$$=-\frac{\sin x}{2\sqrt{\cos x}}$$

EXAMPLES XI.

Differentiate from first principles

1. $\sin 2x$. (Banaras, 1933, 1935, 1941)

2. $\cos ax$ (Banaras, 1955, 1959)

3. $\sqrt{\tan x}$.

4. x^0 (Degrees)

5. $x \sin x$.

6. $\sin (x+h)$

7. $-\cos (x+b)$.

8. $\sec \frac{x}{a}$

9. $(x+a)^n$

10. $\tan^{-1} \frac{x}{a}$.

11. $\cos^2 ax$.

12. $\sec^2 x$.

13. e^{3x+2}

14. e^{x^2}.

CHAPTER IV

FUNDAMENTAL PROPOSITIONS

52. A constant.

Let $y=c$, a constant.

Now, a constant is a quantity which does not change. Hence, whatever δx may be,

$$y+\delta y=c.$$

Therefore, by subtraction,

$\delta y=0,$

i.e., $\dfrac{\delta y}{\delta x}=0,$

so that $\dfrac{dy}{dx}=0.$

Thus, the differential coefficient of a constant is 0*.

53. Product of a constant and a function.

Let $y=cu,$

where c is a constant and u is a function of x.

When x becomes $x+\delta x$, let u become $u+\delta u$ and y become $y+\delta y$.

---

* Geometrically, $y=c$ is the equation of a straight line parallel to the x-axis. At any point on the line it is its own tangent and makes an angle 0 with the x-axis.

Hence $\dfrac{dy}{dx}=0.$

Then $$y+\delta y=c\,(u+\delta u).$$

Therefore, by subtraction,

$$\delta y=c\,\delta u,$$

so that $$\frac{\delta y}{\delta x}=c\frac{\delta u}{\delta x}.$$

Hence, proceeding to the limit,

$$\frac{dy}{dx}=c\frac{du}{dx}.^{*}$$

54. Solved Examples.

(1) The differential coefficient of $10\cos x$ is $-10\sin x$

(2) The first, second, third,...nth diff. coeffs. of ae^x are all ae^x.

55. Sum of two functions.

Let $$y=u+v.$$

Then $y+\delta y=(u+\delta u)+(v+\delta v)$.

$$\therefore \delta y=\delta u+\delta v,$$

so that $$\frac{\delta y}{\delta x}=\frac{\delta u}{\delta x}+\frac{\delta v}{\delta x}.$$

Hence, proceeding to the limit, we have

$$\frac{dy}{dx}=\frac{du}{dx}+\frac{dv}{dx}.$$

Cor. The diff. coeff. of the sum of a set of functions is the sum of the differential coefficients of the several functions.

---

* Geometrically this theorem means that if all the ordinates of a curve are increased in the same ratio, the slope of the curve is increased in the same ratio.

56 Solved Examples.

(1) $$\frac{d}{dx}\left\{x(x^2-3)\right\}=\frac{d}{dx}(x^3-3x)$$

$$=\frac{d}{dx}(x^3)-\frac{d}{dx}(3x)=(3x^2-3)$$

$$=3(x^2-1)$$

(2) $$\frac{d}{dx}\left\{\log x+2\sin x+3e^x\right\}$$

$$=\frac{d}{dx}(\log x)+2\frac{d}{dx}(\sin x)+3\frac{d}{dx}(e^x)$$

$$=\frac{1}{x}+2\cos x+3e^x.$$

EXAMPLES XII

1. Write down the differential coefficient of

$\cos x+2\sin x$, $e^x-\log 2x+x^2$, $\sqrt{x}+\sqrt{a}$,

$\frac{x^4}{4}+\frac{x^3}{3}+\frac{x^2}{2}+1$, $\sin^{-1}x-\cos^{-1}x$, $x^n+a^n x$,

$(x+1)(2x-1)$, $(x-a)(x-b)(x-c)$, $x(ax+b)^2$.

2. Expand the following in series and differentiating term by term, find the differential coefficient of these expressions :—

(1) e^x. (2) $\log(1+x)$. (3) $(1+x)^n$. (4) a^x.

3. Write down the differential coefficients of

(1) $\frac{a-x^2+x}{2x}$. (2) $\frac{b(2x-3)}{ax^2}$.

(3) $\dfrac{a+b\sqrt{x}}{cx\sqrt{x}}$ (4) $\dfrac{a+bx^{3/2}}{c\sqrt[4]{x^5}}$

(5) $\dfrac{ax+b}{\sqrt{x}}$.

57. Product of two Functions.

The differential coefficient of the product of two functions=(First Function)×(Diff. Coeff. of second)+(Second Function)×(Diff. Coeff. of first).

Let $y=uv$.

Then $y+\delta y=(u+\delta u)\ (v+\delta v)$

$=uv+u\delta v+v\delta u+\delta u.\delta v,$

so that $\delta y=u\delta v+v\delta u+\delta u.\delta v.$

Hence $\dfrac{\delta y}{\delta x}=u\dfrac{\delta v}{\delta x}+v\dfrac{\delta u}{\delta x}+\delta u\dfrac{\delta v}{\delta x}.$

Now, $\delta u\to 0$, as $\delta x\to 0$. And $\dfrac{\delta u}{\delta x}$ and $\dfrac{\delta v}{\delta x}$ tend to $\dfrac{du}{dx}$ and $\dfrac{dv}{dx}$ as $\delta x\to 0$.

Hence, proceeding to the limit,

$$\frac{dy}{dx}=u\frac{dv}{dx}+v\frac{du}{dx},$$

Cor. To find out the differential coefficient of the product of a finite number of functions, multiply the differential coefficient of each separate function by the product of all the remaining functions and add up all the results.

For instance, let $y=uvw$

Then $$y'=uvw'+w(uv)'$$
$$=uvw'+w(uv'+u'v)$$
$$=uvw'+wuv'+vwu'.$$

In the same way, if $y=uvwt....,$

$$\frac{dy}{dx}=(vwt...)\frac{du}{dx}+(uwt...)\frac{dv}{dx}+(uvt...)\frac{dw}{dx}+....$$

58. Solved Examples.

(1) Differentiate xe^x, $x^2 \sin x$, $x \log x$.

$$\frac{d}{dx}(xe^x)=x\frac{d(e^x)}{dx}+e^x\frac{d}{dx}(x)$$
$$=xe^x+e^x=(x+1)e^x.$$

$$\frac{d}{dx}(x^2 \sin x)=x^2\frac{d}{dx}(\sin x)+\sin x\frac{d}{dx}(x^2) \quad (1955)$$
$$=x^2 \cos x+2x \sin x.$$

$$\frac{d}{dx}(x \log x)=x\frac{d}{dx}(\log x)+\log x\frac{d}{dx}(x)$$
$$=x\left(\frac{1}{x}\right)+\log x.(1).$$
$$=1+\log x.$$

(2) Differentiate $(x^2+2)(x-3)$ as a product and show that the result is the same if the expressions are multiplied out and then differentiated.

Let $y=(x^2+2)(x-3)$.

Then $$\frac{dy}{dx}=(x^2+2)\frac{d}{dx}(x-3)+(x-3)\frac{d}{dx}(x^2+2)$$
$$=x^2+2+(x-3)(2x)=3x^2-6x+2.$$

If we expand the product we get

$$x^3-3x^2+2x-6.$$

And the differential coefficient is obviously $3x^2-6x+2$.

59. Quotient of two Functions.

The diff. coeff. of the quotient of two functions

$$=\frac{\text{(Denr.) (Diff. Coeff. of Numr.)}-\text{(Numr.) (Diff. Coeff. of Denr.)}}{\text{(Denominator)}^2}$$

Let $y=\dfrac{u}{v}$

Then $y+\delta y=\dfrac{u+\delta u}{v+\delta v}$

and $$\delta y=\frac{u+\delta u}{v+\delta v}-\frac{u}{v}$$

$$=\frac{v\delta u-u\delta v}{v\,(v+\delta v)}=\frac{v\delta u-u\delta v}{v^2\left(1+\dfrac{\delta v}{v}\right)}$$

Therefore, $$\frac{\delta y}{\delta x}=\frac{v\dfrac{\delta u}{\delta x}-u\dfrac{\delta v}{\delta x}}{v^2\left(1+\dfrac{\delta v}{v}\right)}$$

Now, $\delta v\to o$, as $\delta x\to o$.

Hence $$\frac{dy}{dx}=\frac{v\dfrac{du}{dx}-u\dfrac{dv}{dx}}{v^2}.$$

Or thus : As $y = \dfrac{u}{v}$.

$$vy = u.$$

Therefore, by the Theorem for a Product, (§57),

$$v\frac{dy}{dx} + y\frac{dv}{dx} = \frac{du}{dx}.$$

Hence $$\frac{dy}{dx} = \frac{1}{v}\left(\frac{du}{dx} - y\frac{dv}{dx}\right)$$

$$= \frac{1}{v}\left(\frac{du}{dx} - \frac{u}{v}.\frac{dv}{dx}\right)$$

$$= \frac{1}{v^2}\left(v\frac{du}{dx} - u\frac{dv}{dx}\right).$$

60. Solved Examples.

(1) Differentiate $\tan x$ by this method.

$$\frac{d}{dx}(\tan x) = \frac{d}{dx}\left(\frac{\sin x}{\cos x}\right)$$

$$= \frac{\cos x\dfrac{d}{dx}(\sin x) - \sin x\dfrac{d}{dx}(\cos x)}{\cos^2 x}$$

$$= \frac{\cos^2 x + \sin^2 x.}{\cos^2 x}$$

$$= \frac{1}{\cos^2 x} = \sec^2 x.$$

(2) Differentiate $\frac{x^2}{e^x \sin x}$. (1955)

If $y=\frac{x^2}{e^x \sin x}$,

we have $$\frac{dy}{dx}=\frac{e^x \sin x \frac{d}{dx}(x^2) - x^2 \frac{d}{dx}(e^x \sin x)}{e^{2x} \sin^2 x}$$

Now, $$\frac{d}{dx}(e^x \sin x)=e^x \frac{d}{dx}(\sin x)+\sin x \frac{d}{dx}(e^x).$$

$$=e^x \cos x+e^x \sin x.$$

Hence $$\frac{dy}{dx}=\frac{2xe^x \sin x-x^2 (e^x \cos x+e^x \sin x)}{e^{2x} \sin^2 x}$$

$$=xe^x \frac{2\sin x-x(\cos x+\sin x)}{e^{2x} \sin^2 x}$$

(3) Differentiate $\frac{1}{ax+b}$

$$\frac{d}{dx}\left(\frac{1}{ax+b}\right)=\frac{(ax+b)\frac{d}{dx}(1)-1.\frac{d}{dx}(ax+b)}{(ax+b)^2}$$

$$=-\frac{a}{(ax+b)^2}.$$

(4) Differentiate $\frac{2x+3}{5x-1}$. (Banaras, 1951)

First Method. Let $y = \dfrac{2x+3}{5x-1}$.

Then $\dfrac{dy}{dx} = \dfrac{(5x-1)\dfrac{d}{dx}(2x+3) - (2x+3)\dfrac{d}{dx}(5x-1)}{(5x-1)^2}$.

$= \dfrac{2(5x-1)-5(2x+3)}{(5x-1)^2} = -\dfrac{17}{(5x-1)^2}$.

Second Method.

$$\frac{dy}{dx} = \frac{1}{5x-1}\frac{d}{dx}(2x+3) + (2x+3)\frac{d}{dx}\left(\frac{1}{5x-1}\right)$$

$$= \frac{2}{5x-1} + (2x+3).\frac{-5}{(5x-1)^2} \text{(Solved Ex. 3)}$$

$$= \frac{2(5x-1)-5(2x+3)}{(5x-1)^2}$$

$$= -\frac{17}{(5x-1)^2}.$$

Third Method

$$\frac{2x+3}{5x-1} = \frac{2}{5} + \left(\frac{2x+3}{5x-1} - \frac{2}{5}\right)$$

$$= \frac{2}{5} + \frac{17}{5(5x-1)}.$$

Hence $\dfrac{dy}{dx} = \dfrac{17}{5}\dfrac{d}{dx}\left(\dfrac{1}{5x-1}\right)$

$$=\frac{17}{5}\cdot\frac{-5}{(5x-1)^2} \qquad \text{(Solved Ex. 3)}$$

$$=\frac{-17}{(5x-1)^2}.$$

EXAMPLES XIII.

Differentiate

1. $x^2\cos x$ (Banaras 1944), $x^3 e^x$, $x^n e^x$, $2^x\sin x$, $x^2\log x$, $x\sin^{-1}x\log x$ (1956), $x^2 e^x\tan x$, $\sqrt{x}\sec x\,\text{cosec}\, x$.

2. $\dfrac{x^2}{\sin x}$, $\text{cosec}\, x$, $\dfrac{\cos x}{x^4}$, $\dfrac{x^3}{\tan x}$, $\dfrac{c^2 x}{x^2+\sin x}$, $\dfrac{x^2\cos x}{e^x}$,

$\dfrac{x}{e^x\log x\sin x}$, $\dfrac{3\sec x}{\sqrt{x}}$ (Banaras 1952)

3. $(x^2-4\sqrt{x})\log x$, $e^x(\tan x+\cos x)$, $(x+x^2)e^x\log x$, $(3+8e^x)\sec x$, $(5x-3e^x)\log x$, $x\sin x+\cos x$.

4. $\dfrac{x^2}{\sin x+\cos x}$, $\dfrac{\sec x-\tan x}{\sec x+\tan x}$, $\dfrac{(e^x+3)x}{\sin x+2}$

5. $\dfrac{a-x}{a+x}$, $\dfrac{a+x}{a-x}$, $\dfrac{ax+b}{cx+d}$, $\dfrac{\sin x+\cos x}{\sin x-\cos x}$, $\dfrac{\sin x-\cos x}{\sin x+\cos x}$ (1956)

6. $\dfrac{x^2-a^2}{x^2+a^2}$, $\dfrac{1+2x+3x^2}{1-2x+3x^2}$, $\dfrac{\sqrt{x}+1}{\sqrt{x}-1}$, $\dfrac{(x+2)(x+3)}{x+1}$,

$\dfrac{px^2+qx+r}{rx^2+qx+p}$.

7. $x \cos^2 x$, $2x \sin^2 x$, $e^x \log x \cos^2 x$.

(*Hint.* $\cos^2 x = \dfrac{1+\cos 2x}{2}$. Use Ex. XI Q. 2)

61. Function of a Function.

Sometimes we come across a function of an expression which is itself a function of the independent variable x.

For example, if $y=(ax+b)^n$, y is a function of $(ax+b)$, while this latter expression is itself a function of x. If we put

$$u=ax+b,$$

we have
$$y=u^n,$$

so that y is a function of u, while u is function of x. That is to say, y is a function of a function of x.

As another example, the relation

$$y=a \cos (2x+3)+b$$

may be expressed as

$$y=a \cos u+b,$$

and
$$u=2x+3.$$

Let
$$y=F(u),$$

where
$$u=f(x).$$

When x is changed to $x+\delta x$, let u and y be changed to $u+\delta u$ and $y+\delta y$ respectively.

But
$$\frac{\delta y}{\delta x}=\frac{\delta y}{\delta u}\times\frac{\delta u}{\delta x}. \qquad (61.1)$$

$$\underset{\delta x\to 0}{\mathrm{Lt}}\ \frac{\delta y}{\delta x}=\underset{\delta x\to 0}{\mathrm{Lt}}\left\{\frac{\delta y}{\delta u}\times\frac{\delta u}{\delta x}\right\}.$$

Now, when $\delta x \to 0$, $\delta u \to 0$. Hence

$$\underset{\delta x \to 0}{\text{Lt}} \frac{\delta y}{\delta x} = \underset{\delta u \to 0}{\text{Lt}} \frac{\delta y}{\delta u} \times \underset{\delta x \to 0}{\text{Lt}} \frac{\delta u}{\delta x}.$$

$$\text{i.e.,} \quad \frac{dy}{dx} = \frac{dy}{du} \cdot \frac{du}{dx}. \tag{61.2}$$

Or, in words,

$$\frac{d(\text{first function})}{dx} = \frac{d\,(\text{first function})}{d\,(\text{second function})} \times \frac{d\,(\text{second function})}{dx}$$

The student is apt to think that equation (61.2) is as obvious as equation (61.1), and that we could put down eqn. (61.2) without having recourse to eqn. (61.1). But it should be borne in mind that in (61.1) δu, δx and δy are separate quantities and hence δu in the numerator cancels δu in the denominator. But in (61.2) dx, dy, du are not separate quantities. $\frac{du}{dx}$ and $\frac{dy}{du}$ are the results of a process; they are not the quotients of '*du* by *dx*' and '*dy* by *du*'. Hence it would be absurd to say that in (61.2) *du* in the numerator and *du* in the denominator cancel each other and yield the left-hand side of the eqn.

62. Solved Examples.

Differentiate $(2x-1)^7$ and $\cos(\log x)$.

Let $\quad u=2x-1$,

so that $\quad y=u^7$.

Then $\quad \frac{dy}{dx}=\frac{dy}{du} \cdot \frac{du}{dx}.$

$$=\frac{d(u^7)}{du}\cdot\frac{d(2x-1)}{dx}$$

$$=7u^6.2=14\ (2x-1)^6$$

Again, putting $u=\log x$, we have

$$y=\cos u.$$

Where $u=\log x$.

$$\text{Hence}\ \frac{dy}{dx}=\frac{dy}{du}\cdot\frac{du}{dx}=\frac{d(\cos u)}{du}\cdot\frac{d(\log x)}{dx}$$

$$=-\sin u\frac{1}{x}=-\frac{1}{x}\sin(\log x).$$

63. **The above rule may be extended.** Let

$$y=F(u),$$

where $u=\phi\ (v)$

and $v=f(x)$,

For example, the relation

$$y=e^{\sin(2x+5)}$$

may be expressed as

$$y=e^u,$$

$$u=\sin v,$$

and $v=2x+5$.

We have $\dfrac{dy}{dx}=\dfrac{dy}{du}\cdot\dfrac{du}{dx}$.

But $\dfrac{du}{dx}=\dfrac{du}{dv}\cdot\dfrac{dv}{dx}$

Hence $\dfrac{dy}{dx}=\dfrac{dy}{du}\cdot\dfrac{du}{dv}\cdot\dfrac{dv}{dx}$.

A similar result holds for any finite number of functions. Thus.

$$\frac{d\,(\text{1st function})}{dx}=\frac{d\,(\text{1st function})}{d\,(\text{2nd function})}\times\frac{d(\text{2nd function})}{d(\text{3rd function})}\times\ldots$$

$$\times\frac{d(\text{last function})}{dx}$$

64. Solved Examples.

(1) In the example given above

$$\frac{dy}{dx}=\frac{dy}{du}.\frac{du}{dv}.\frac{dv}{dx}=\frac{d(e^u)}{du}.\frac{d\,(\sin v)}{dv}.\frac{d\,(2x+5)}{dx}$$

$$=e^u.\cos v.\,2=2\cos(2x+5)\,e^{\sin(2x+5)}$$

(2) Differentiate $\log\{\tan(\cos\sqrt{x})\}$ (Banaras 1951)

Putting y for this expression we have

$$y=\log u,$$

where $u=\tan v,$

$$v=\cos w,$$

and $w=\sqrt{x}.$

Hence $\dfrac{dy}{dx}=\dfrac{dy}{du}.\dfrac{du}{dv}.\dfrac{dv}{dw}.\dfrac{dw}{dx}$

$$=\frac{d(\log u)}{du}.\frac{d(\tan v)}{dv}.\frac{d(\cos w)}{dw}.\frac{d\sqrt{x}}{dx}.$$

$$=\frac{1}{u}\sec^2 v\,(-\sin w).\frac{1}{2\sqrt{x}}$$

$$= \frac{1}{\tan v} . \sec^2(\cos w)\ (-\sin w) . \frac{1}{2\sqrt{x}}$$

$$= -\frac{1}{2\sqrt{x}} \sin\sqrt{x}.\ \sec^2(\cos\sqrt{x}).\ \cot(\cos\sqrt{x})$$

65. Interchange of the Dependent and Independent Variables

By the last theorem we have

$$\frac{dt}{dy} . \frac{dy}{dx} = \frac{dt}{dx} .$$

Suppose now that $t=x$. Then we have

$$\frac{dx}{dy} . \frac{dy}{dx} = \frac{dx}{dx} = \underset{h\to o}{\text{Lt}} \frac{(x+h)-x}{h} = 1.$$

Thus we obtain the result

$$\frac{dy}{dx} = \frac{1}{\frac{dx}{dy}} .$$

This result will be manifest from a figure too. For $\frac{dy}{dx}$ and $\frac{dx}{dy}$ are respectively the tangent and cotangent of the angle ψ.

66. The last formula is very useful in differentiating inverse functions. For example, let

$$y=\sin^{-1} x.$$

Then $x = \sin y.$

Therefore $\frac{dx}{dy} = \cos y.$

Hence $\dfrac{dy}{dx}=\dfrac{1}{\dfrac{dx}{dy}}=\dfrac{1}{\cos y}=\dfrac{1}{\sqrt{(1-\sin^2 y)}}=\dfrac{1}{\sqrt{(1-x^2)}}.$

And since $\cos^{-1}x=\dfrac{\pi}{2}-\sin^{-1}x,$

we also have $\dfrac{d(\cos^{-1}x)}{dx}=-\dfrac{d(\sin^{-1}x)}{dx}=-\dfrac{+1}{\sqrt{(1-x^2)}}$

Generally, let $y=f^{-1}(x)$.

Then $x=f(y)$,

and $\dfrac{dx}{dy}=f'(y)$

Therefore $\dfrac{dy}{dx}=\dfrac{1}{\dfrac{dx}{dy}}=\dfrac{1}{f'(y)}=\dfrac{1}{f'[f^{-1}(x)]}.$

In the example chosen above 'f' is 'sin' ; hence 'f'' will mean 'cos'. . So that

$$\frac{d(\sin^{-1}x)}{dx}=\frac{1}{\cos(\sin^{-1}x)}=\frac{1}{\sqrt{(1-x^2)}}.$$

EXAMPLES XIV

Differentiate

1. $\cos x\cos 2x$, $\cos\sqrt{x}$ (Banaras 1941).
   $x\cos^2 x$ (Banaras 1952), $\sin(e^x)$.

2. $\dfrac{1}{(2x+3)^4}$, $(ax+b)^n$.

3. $\sqrt{(x^2+ax+1)}$, $\dfrac{1}{\sqrt{(ax^2+bx+c)}}$.

4. $\sin^n x \cos^n x$, $\sin [\tan (\cos x)]$.

5. $\cos \log x$ (1955, 1958), $\sin \cos \log x$, (Banaras 1952)

$\dfrac{\log \log x}{x}$ (Banaras 1941)

6. $\sin^{-1} \dfrac{1}{\sqrt{(1+x^2)}}$, $e^{\sqrt{\cos x}}$, $\left[\dfrac{x\cos^{-1}x}{\sqrt{(1-x^2)}}\right]$,

$\tan^{-1}\left(\dfrac{\cos x}{1+\sin x}\right)$ (Banaras 1948, 1955)

7. $\dfrac{(2x-1)^2}{(3x+2)^2}$, $\left(\sqrt{x}-\dfrac{1}{\sqrt{x}}\right)^3$, $\dfrac{x^n}{(a+x)^n}$

8. $\log \dfrac{a+bx}{a-bx}$, $\log [x-\sqrt{(x^2-1)}]$, $(x^3+x^2+1) \log x$.

(Banaras 1952).

9. $2^{x \sin x}$ (1956), $\sqrt{(\cos\sqrt{\sin\sqrt{x}})}$, (Banaras 1946, 1956).

$\log \left[e^x\left(\dfrac{x-2}{x+2}\right)\right]^{3/4}$

10. Differentiate $\sec^{-1}x$, $\tan^{-1}x$, $\text{vers}^{-1}x$ by the method of interchange of variables.

11. Differentiate $\dfrac{1}{x}$, $\dfrac{1}{x^2}$, $\dfrac{1}{(ax+b)^3}$ by the method of interchange of variables.

12. If $x=2a \sin^{-1} \sqrt{\left[\dfrac{y}{2a}\right]} - \sqrt{(2ay-y^2)}$, (1956)

then $$\frac{dy}{dx}=\sqrt{\left(\frac{2a-y}{y}\right)}.$$

67. Logarithmic Differentiation. The Form u^v

When y is of the form u^v, where both u and v are functions of x, it is desirable to take logarithms before proceeding to differentiation.

If $y=u^v$,

$\log y=v \log u.$

Therefore, $$\frac{1}{y}.\frac{dy}{dx}=\frac{dv}{dx}\log u+v.\frac{1}{u}.\frac{du}{dx},$$

so that $$\frac{dy}{dx}=u^{v-1}\left(u\frac{dv}{dx}\log u+v\frac{du}{dx}\right).$$

This compound process is known as Logarithmic Differentiation.

68. Solved Examples.

(1) If $y=x^x$, (Banaras 1943, 1957)

$\log y=x \log x.$

$$\therefore \frac{1}{y}.\frac{dy}{dx}=\log x+1.$$

Hence $$\frac{dy}{dx}=y(\log x+1)=x^x(\log^x+1).$$

(2) Differentiate $x^{\sin x}+(\tan x)^{\cos x}$.

Here we should not take logarithms directly.

Let $u=x^{\sin x}$. (Banaras 1949, 1954)

Then $\log u=\sin x \log x.$

$$\therefore \frac{1}{u}\cdot\frac{du}{dx}=\sin x\cdot\frac{1}{x}+\cos x \log x.$$

Hence $$\frac{du}{dx}=x^{\sin x}\left(\frac{\sin x}{x}+\cos x \log x\right).\quad (68.1)$$

Again, let $v=(\tan x)^{\cos x}$

Then $\log v=\cos x \log (\tan x)$.

$$\therefore \frac{1}{v}\cdot\frac{dv}{dx}=-\sin x \log (\tan x)$$

$$+\cos x.\ \frac{1}{\tan x}.\ \sec^2 x.$$

Hence $$\frac{dv}{dx}=(\tan x)^{\cos x}\ [\operatorname{cosec} x-\sin x \log (\tan x)].$$

(68.2)

And the diff. coeff. required is the sum of (68.1) and (68.2).

69. The above proposition has three important particular cases :

1. Let v be a constant and u a function of x.

Then $\frac{dv}{dx}=0$, and the above proposition reduces to

$$\frac{dy}{dx}=v.\ u^{v-1}\ \frac{du}{dx},$$

as we might naturally expect from the form of the function.

For example, let $y=(ax+b)^n$.

Then $$\frac{dy}{dx}=n\,(ax+b)^{n-1}\frac{d}{dx}(ax+b)$$

$$=na\,(ax+b)^{n-1}.$$

As a particular case, when $a=1$, $b=0$,

$$\frac{d}{dx}(x^n)=nx^{n-1} \qquad (cf.\ \S\ 31)$$

II. If u be a constant and v a function of x, $\frac{du}{dx}=0$, and the proposition becomes

$$\frac{dy}{dx}=u^v \log u\,\frac{dv}{dx}.$$

For example, if $y=a^{cx+d}$

we have $$\frac{dy}{dx}=a^v \log a.\ \frac{d}{dx}(cx+d)$$

$$=c \log a.\ a^{cx+d}$$

As a particular case, if $c=1$, $d=0$.

$$\frac{d}{dx}(a^x)=a^x \log a \qquad (\ cf.\ \S 32)$$

III. Let u and v be both functions of x. Then the general formula

$$\frac{dy}{dx}=u^v \log u\,\frac{dv}{dx}+vu^{v-1}\frac{du}{dx}$$

is a combination of the above two particular cases. Hence, instead of taking logarithms, we might first consider u constant and differentiate and then consider v constant and differentiate. The sum of the two will give us the result desired. For example, let us revert back to the function

$$x^{\sin x} \qquad \text{(cf. solved Ex. 2 of § 68)}$$

Considering $\sin x$ as a constant, the diff. coeff. is

$$\sin x . x^{\sin x - 1}$$

Now, consider x as a constant. Putting K for x, the function becomes

$$K^{\sin x}$$

the diff. coeff. of which is

$$K^{\sin x} \log K . \cos x, \text{ i.e. } x^{\sin x} \log x . \cos x.$$

And the diff. coeff. required is the sum of the two.

EXAMPLES XV.

Differentiate

1. $(ax+b)^{cx+d}$, $(\cos x)^x$, $e^{x \sin x}$ (1955)

2. $(\cos^{-1} x)^x$, $x^{\cos^{-1} x}$, $(\sqrt{x})e^x \log x$, e^{x^x}

3. $(\sec x)^{\tan x} + (\tan x)^{\sec x}$, $x^{\cos x} + (\cos x)^x$.

4. $x^{x^2} + x^{2x}$, $(1+\cos x)^{\sin x}$.

5. $e^{\sin x} (\log \tan x)$.

CHAPTER V

THE MEANING OF INTEGRATION

70. The Integral.

Let $y=x^2$

be a function of x. Let us study the behaviour of this function for the interval $x=2$ to $x=3$. We divide the interval (2,3) into five equal parts each of length ·2. When $x=2$, $y=2^2$; when $x=2{\cdot}2$, $y=(2{\cdot}2)^2$; when $x=2{\cdot}4$, $y=(2{\cdot}4)^2$ and so on. Let us multiply each of these values of y by the length of the sub-interval and find the sum. The sum will be

$$({\cdot}2)\ (2)^2+({\cdot}2)\ (2{\cdot}2)^2+({\cdot}2)\ (2{\cdot}4)^2+({\cdot}2)\ (2{\cdot}6)^2+({\cdot}2)\ (2{\cdot}8)^{2*}$$

$$=({\cdot}2)\ \{2^2+(2{\cdot}2)^2+(2{\cdot}4)^2+(2{\cdot}6)^2+(2{\cdot}8)^2\}.$$

We shall denote the sum by S. Thus

$$S=5{\cdot}8.$$

Now, let us divide the interval (2,3) into ten equal parts each of length ·1 and form a similar sum. Then, in this case

$$S=(1)\{2^2+(2{\cdot}1)^2+(2{\cdot}2)^2+(2{\cdot}3)^2+(2{\cdot}4)^2+(2{\cdot}5)^2+(2{\cdot}6)^2 +(2{\cdot}7)^2+(2{\cdot}8)^2+(2{\cdot}9)^2\}=6$$

---

*For simplicity we exclude the extreme value $x=3$. But as will be seen later on, the final conclusion will not be affected even if we include this value.

Lastly, if we divide the interval into 20 equal parts —the length of each will consequently be ·05—and find a similar sum, we shall have

$$S=(\cdot 05)\{2^2+(2\cdot 05)^2+(2\cdot 1)^2+(2.15)^2+(2\cdot 2)^2+(2\cdot 25)^2+\ldots (2\cdot 85)^2+(2\cdot 9)^2+(2\cdot 95)^2\}=6\cdot 2,$$

approximately.

Let us prepare a table of these results thus :

Number of intervals	5	10	20
Length of each interval	·2	·1	·0
Value of S	5·8	6	6·2

A study of this table reveals the fact that as the number of intervals gets larger and consequently the length of each interval gets smaller, the value of S goes on increasing. This raises the presumption that if we still increase the number of intervals and consequently decrease the length of each, the value of S will increase further. Suppose now that the number of intervals is increased indefinitely and consequently the length of each is diminished indefinitely. Is it possible that the value of S may tend to a definite limit when the number of intervals tends to infinity and the length of each tends to zero ?

Let the number of intervals between (2,3) be n and the length of each be h. Then

$$3=2+nh. \tag{70·1}$$

And $S=h\{2^2+(2+h)^2+(2+2h)^2+\ldots(2+\overline{n-1}h)^2\}$

$$=h\sum_{r=0}^{n-1}(2+rh)^2$$

$$=h\left\{\sum_{r=0}^{n-1}2^2+4h\sum_{r=0}^{n-1}r+h^2\sum_{r=0}^{n-1}r^2\right\}$$

$$=h[n.\ 2^2+4h\ (1+2+3+\ldots+\overline{n-1})$$
$$+\ h^2\ [\{1^2+\ 2^2+3^2\ +\ldots+\ (n-1)^2\}]$$

$$=h\ \{n.2^2+2h.n(n-1)+\frac{h^2}{6}(n-1)n(2n-1)\}$$

$$=2^2nh+2nh(nh-h)+\tfrac{1}{6}nh(nh-h)(2nh-h).$$

But, by (70.1), we have $nh=1$. Hence

$S=2^2+2(1-h)+\frac{1}{6}(1-h)\ (2-h).$

And the limit of this when $h\to 0$, is

$$2^2+2+\tfrac{1}{3}=6\tfrac{1}{3}.$$

So, we see that in this particular case at least, S tends to a definte limit as $n\to\infty$ and consequently $h\to 0$.

Now, let us consider the interval (a, b) of x instead of (2, 3). We divide the interval into n equal sub-intervals each of length h, so that $b=a+nh$. Let

$S=h\{a^2+(a+h)^2+(a+2h)^2+\ldots+(a+\overline{n-1}h)^2\}$

$$=h\sum_{r=0}^{n-1}(a+rh)^2$$

$$=h\left[\sum_{r=0}^{n-1}a^2+2ah\sum_{r=0}^{n-1}r+h^2\sum_{r=0}^{n-1}r^2\right]$$

$$=h[n.a^2+2ah\{1+2+3+\ldots+\overline{n-1}\}$$
$$+h^2\{1^2+2^2+3^2+\ldots+(n-1)^2\}$$

$$=h\left[n.a^2+anh(n-1)+\frac{n(n-1)(2n-1)h^2}{6}\right]$$

$$=nh.a^2+anh\ (nh-h)\ +\tfrac{1}{6}nh(nh-h)(2nh-h)$$

But $b=a+nh$, *i.e.*, $nh=b-a$.

Hence $S=a^2(b-a)+a(b-a)(b-a-h)$

$$+\tfrac{1}{6}\ (b-a)\ (b-a-h)\ (2b-2a-h)$$

and the limit of this when $h\to 0$, is

$$a^2(b-a)+a(b-a)^2+\tfrac{1}{3}(b-a)^3 = \frac{b^3}{3}-\frac{a^3}{3}$$

The limit $\dfrac{b^3}{3}-\dfrac{a^3}{3}$ is called the Integral of the function x^2 with respect to x between the limits a and b. And this result agrees with the limit arrived at in the particular case considered above; for when $a=2$, $b=3$, it becomes $6\frac{1}{3}$

Generally speaking, let

$$y=f(x)$$

be a finite function of x, and let (a, b) be the interval of values of x under consideration. We divide the interval into n equal parts each of length h.* Thus

$$b=a+nh.$$

Corresponding to each of the intermediary values—a, $a+h$, $a+2h$, $a+3h$,..., $a+\overline{n-1}h$—we put down the values of y:

$$f(a),\ f(a+h),\ f(a+2h),\dots\ f\ (a+\overline{n-1}h)$$

---

* Here too we might use δx instead of h. We shall use them interchangeably.

Then the limit

$$\underset{h \to 0}{\text{Lt}}\, h[f\,(a)+f(a+h)+f(a+2h)+\ldots f(a+\overline{n-1}h)]^{**}$$

is called "the Integral of the function $f(x)$ with respect to x between the limits a and b" and is written as

$$\int_b^a f(x)\ dx.$$

And the process of finding this limit is called "Integration" of $f(x)$. Thus

$$\int_a^b f(x)dx = \underset{h \to 0}{\text{Lt}}\ h\ [f\ (a+h) + f\ (a+2h) + \ldots +$$

$$f(a+\overline{n-1}h)]$$

So, the sign

$$\int_a^b f(x)\ dx$$

means that we are to

(1) put down $a, a+h, a+2h, \ldots a, +\overline{n-1}h$ in place of x and thus find out the values of $f(a), (a+h), f(a+2h), \ldots\ldots\ldots\ldots,$ $f(a+\overline{n-1}h)$,

(2) find the sum of all these,

(3) multiply the sum by h,

** It is easy to see that this limit is finite. For, if $f(a+rh)$ be the greatest term the sum is

$$< nh\, f(a+rh)$$

$$i.e., < (b-a) f(a+rh)$$

which is finite as by hypothesis $f(x)$ is finite for all values of x between a and b.

(4) substitute for n from the relation

$$b=a+nh,$$

(5) find the limit of the result when $h \to 0$.

This will give us the integral required.

71. If, in the series we take the sum of $(n+1)$ terms

$$h[f(a)+f(a+h)+\ldots+f(a+\overline{n-1}h)+f(a+nh)]$$

instead of the first n terms, the only difference will be the addition of the last term

$$hf(a+nh) \qquad \text{or} \qquad hf(b)$$

which tends to zero when h tends to zero. Hence the limit would be the same if we include the extreme value $x=b$ in the sum.

72. Solved Examples.

(1) Evaluate $\int_a^b \cos x \, dx$.

We are to find the limit of

$$h\,[\cos a+\cos (a+h)+\cos (a+2h)+\ldots+\cos (a+\overline{n-1}\,h)],$$

i.e., of $h \dfrac{\cos\left(a+\dfrac{n-1}{2}h\right)\sin\dfrac{nh}{2}}{\sin\dfrac{h}{2}}$

But $\quad nh=b-a.$

Hence the limit required

$$=\underset{h\to 0}{\text{Lt}}\left[\frac{h}{2\sin\frac{h}{2}}.2\cos\left(a+\frac{b-a-h}{2}\right)\sin\frac{b-a}{2}\right]$$

$$=\underset{h\to 0}{\text{Lt}}\frac{\frac{h}{2}}{\sin\frac{h}{2}}\left\{\sin\left(b-\frac{h}{2}\right)-\sin\left(a-\frac{h}{2}\right)\right\}$$

$=\sin b-\sin a.$

(2) Calculate $\int_a^b \frac{1}{x^2}\,dx$

The integral required is the limit when $h\to 0$. of

$$h\left[\frac{1}{a^2}+\frac{1}{(a+h)^2}+\frac{1}{(a+2h)^2}+\ldots+\frac{1}{b^2}\right]$$

This expression,

$$>h\left[\frac{1}{a(a+h)}+\frac{1}{(a+h)(a+2h)}+\ldots+\frac{1}{b\,(b+h)}\right]$$

$$i.\,e., > \left(\frac{1}{a}-\frac{1}{a+h}\right)+\left(\frac{1}{a+h}-\frac{1}{a+2h}\right)+\ldots$$

$$\mp\left(\frac{1}{b}-\frac{1}{b+h}\right)$$

$$i.e., > \frac{1}{a}-\frac{1}{b+h}$$

Also, the expression

$$<h\left[\frac{1}{(a-h)a}+\frac{1}{a(a+h)}+\frac{1}{(a+h)\,(a+2h)}+\ldots+\frac{1}{(b-h)b}\right]$$

$$i.\,e., < \left(\frac{1}{a-h} - \frac{1}{a}\right) + \left(\frac{1}{a} - \frac{1}{a+h}\right) + \left(\frac{1}{a+h} - \frac{1}{a+2h}\right) + \ldots + \left(\frac{1}{-h} - \frac{1}{b}\right),$$

$$i.\,e., < \frac{1}{a-h} - \frac{1}{b}$$

And when $h \to 0$, each of these becomes

$$\frac{1}{a} - \frac{1}{b}.$$

Hence $\displaystyle\int_a^b \frac{1}{x^2}\,dx = \frac{1}{a} - \frac{1}{b}.$

EXAMPLES XVI.

Evaluate

1. $\int_a^b e^x\,dx$ 2. $\int_a^b e^{x}\,dx$ 3. $\int_a^b x\,dx$

4. $\int_1^2 x^3\,dx$ 5. $\int_0^\pi \sin\theta\,d\theta.$

73. Geometrical Significance. Area

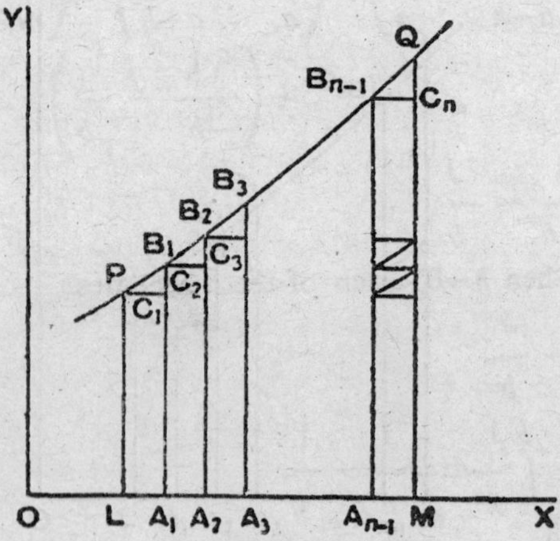

Fig. 11

Let P, Q be a curve whose equation is

$$y=f(x).$$

Let P, Q be two points on the curve with abscissae a, b.
If PL, QM are perp. to OX, $LM=b-a$.

Let LM be divided into n equal parts LA_1, A_1A_2. A_2A_3,..., $A_{n-1}M$ each of length h. Erect ordinates on the points A_1, A_2, A_3,...A_{n-1}, so that the lengths of these ordinates LP, A_1B_1, A_2B_2,......$A_{n-1}B_{n-1}$ are

$$f(a), f(a+h), f(a+2h), \ldots, f(a+\overline{n-1}h).$$

Complete the rectangles BA_1, B_1A_2, B_2A_3,........., $B_{n-1}M$. Then the area of these rectangles falls short of the area $PLMQ$ by the sum of the small figures

$PB_1 \ C_1, \ B_1 \ B_2C_2, \ldots\ldots, \ B_{n-1} \ QC_n$. By moving these figures parallel to the x-axis it can be shown that their sum is less than the last rectangle $B_{n-1} \ M$.

Now, let n, the number of the parts, be increased indefinitely and consequently let h, the length of each be decreased indefinitely. Ultimately, when $n \to \infty$ and $h \to 0$, the area of the rect. $B_{n-1} \ M$ will tend to zero because of its breadth h, so that the sum of the figs. $PB_1C_1, \ B_1B_2C_2, \ldots\ldots\ldots\ldots$will vanish, and the limit of the sum of the rects. $PA_1, \ B_1A_2 \ldots$will be the area $PLMQ$. And the value of this limit will be

$$\underset{h \to 0}{\text{Lt}} \ h \ [f(a)+f(a+h)+f(a+2h)+\ldots+f(a+\overline{n-1}h)],$$

$$i.e., \int_a^b f(x)dx.$$

74. If, in the fig. 12 on page 96 we consider the rects. $A_1D_1, \ A_2 \ D_2 \ldots\ldots\ldots MD_{n-1}$ instead of the rects. $A_1 \ P$, $AB_1, \ldots\ldots MB_{n-1}$ we would arrive at the expression

$$h \ [f(a+h)+f(a+2h)+\ldots+f(a+\overline{n-1}h)+f(a+nh)].$$

The difference between this expression and (73·1) is that here we have $h f(a+nh)$ or $h f(b)$ in place of $h f(a)$. As either of these expressions vanishes when $h \to 0$, the limit will be the same as that of (73.1).

75. The aim of Integral Calculus.

Thus it would appear that the aim of Integral Calculus is to obtain some general method of finding the areas of curves. And, in reality, it is the result of an attempt to find out such a method. When such a method

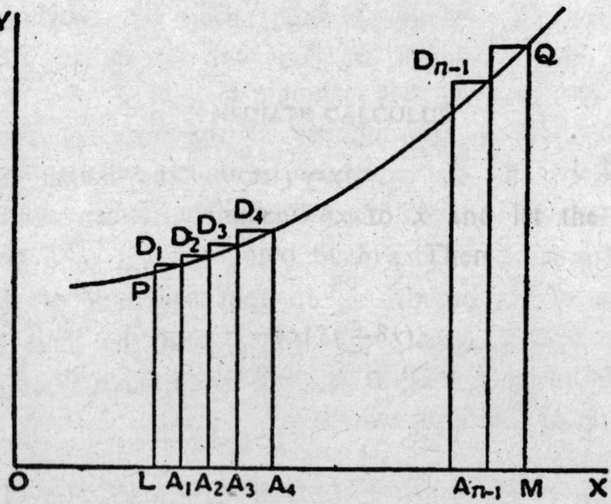

Fig. 12

has been found out, it can be utilised in finding the volumes of Solids of Revolution, and the surfaces of such solids and the lengths of curves, as will be manifest from the sequel.

76. Solved Examples.

(1) Find the area of the curve.

$$y=e^{-x}$$

from $x=2$ to $x=3$.

The area required is

$$\int_2^3 e^{-x}dx$$

$$= \underset{h\to 0}{\text{Lt}}\; h\left[e^{-2}+e^{-(2+h)}+e^{-(2+2h)}+\ldots+e^{-\{2+(\overline{n-1}h)\}}\right]$$

where $2+nh=3$.

So, the area

$$=e^{-2}\underset{h\to 0}{\text{Lt}}\, h\,[1+e^{-h}+e^{-2h}+\dots\dots e^{-(n-1)h}]$$

$$=e^{-2}\underset{h\to 0}{\text{Lt}}\, h\frac{1-e^{-nh}}{1-e^{-h}}=\underset{h\to 0}{\text{Lt}}\frac{e^{-2}-e^{-(2+nh)}}{1-e^{-h}}$$

But $nh=3-2=1$. Hence the area is

$$\underset{h\to 0}{\text{Lt}}\, h\frac{e^{-2}-e^{-3}}{1-e^{-h}}=\underset{h\to 0}{\text{Lt}}\frac{h}{e^{-1}}\cdot e^{h}\,(e^{-2}-e^{-3})$$

$$=e^{-2}-e^{-3}$$ (See § 8).

(2) Find the area of the figure bounded by the curve $x^2=4\,ay$, the x-axis and the ordinate $x=c$.

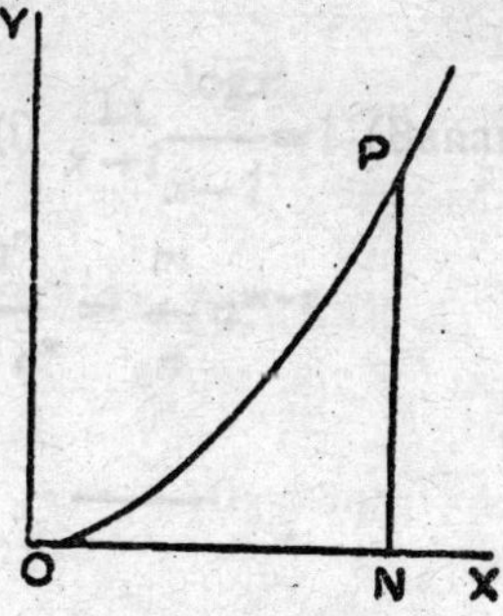

Fig. 13

Here, we are to find the area of the figure ONP as shown in the diagram, where $ON=c$.

The area required

$$=\int_0^c y\,dx=\int_0^c \frac{x^2}{4a}dx$$

$$=\underset{h\to 0}{\mathrm{Lt}}\ h\left[\frac{h^2}{4a}+\frac{(2h)^2}{4a}+\frac{(3h)^2}{4a}+\ldots+\frac{(\overline{n-1}h)^2}{4a}\right]$$

$$=\frac{1}{4a}\underset{h\to 0}{\mathrm{Lt}}\ h^3\,[1^2+2^2+3^2+\ldots+(n-1)^2]$$

$$=\frac{1}{4a}\underset{h\to 0}{\mathrm{Lt}}\ h^3\frac{(n-1)\,n\,(2n-1)}{6}$$

$$=\frac{1}{4a}\underset{h\to 0}{\mathrm{Lt}}\frac{(nh-h)\,nh\,(2nh-h)}{6}.$$

But, in this case, $nh=c$. Hence the area

$$=\frac{1}{4a}\underset{h\to 0}{\mathrm{Lt}}\frac{(c-h)\,c\,(2c-h)}{6}$$

$$=\frac{1}{4a}\cdot\frac{2c^3}{6}=\frac{c^3}{12a}.$$

EXAMPLES XVII.

Find the area of the curve

1. $y=c\sin bx$ from $x=0$ to $x=\dfrac{\pi}{2b}$.

2. $y=a\cos^2 bx$ from $x=0$ to $x=\dfrac{\pi}{b}$.

3. $y=3x^2+2x$ from $x=1$ to $x=2$.

4. Find that ordinate of parabola $x^2=4ay$, between which, x-axis and the curve the area comprised is $\frac{2a^2}{3}$.

5. Find the area of the triangle formed by the straight lines

$$y=0,\ x=h, \text{ and } y=x \tan \alpha.$$

6. Find the area of the trapezium formed by the straight lines

$$x=-a,\ x=-b,\ y=0,\ 2x+3y=0.$$

77. Volume of a Solid of Revolution.

Suppose a curve PQ revolves round the x-axis and we are required to find the volume of the solid thus formed.

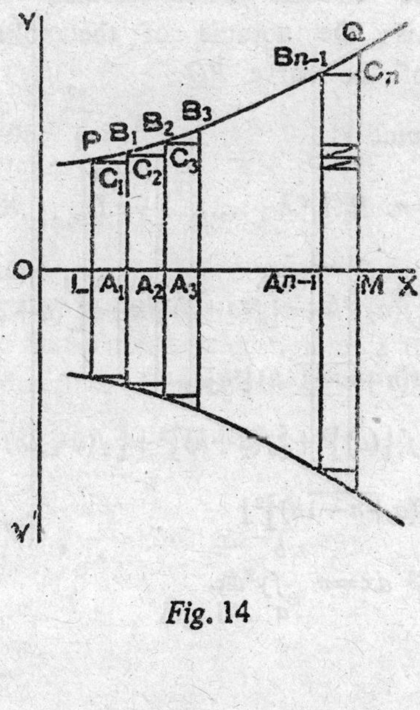

Fig. 14

Let $y=f(x)$;

be the equation of the curve and let us form rects. PA_1, B_1A_2,...as we did in fig. (11). As the curve PQ revolves round OX, these rects. trace circular discs of equal thickness h and volumes

$$\pi.PL^2.h,\ \pi B_1A_1{}^2.h,\ldots\pi.B_{n-1}A^2{}_{n-1}h.$$

The small solids formed by the figs. PB_1C_1, $B_1B_2C_2$,......can be shown to be together less than the solid formed by the rect. $B_{n-1}M$. And as $h\to 0$, the volume of this last named solid tends to zero : and so also the sum of the volumes of solids formed by the figs. PB_1C_1, $B_1B_2C_2$,.........Hence the limit of the volume of the circular discs formed by the rects. PA_1, B_1A_2,......is the volume of the solid formed by the revolution of the curve PQ.

Thus the volume is

$$\underset{h\to 0}{\text{Lt}}\ [\pi.\ PL^2\ h+\pi.\ B_1A_1{}^2.h+\ldots\ldots\ldots+\pi.B_{n-1}\ A^2{}_{n-1}h]$$

$$=\underset{h\to 0}{\text{Lt}}\ [\pi\{f(a)\}^2h+\pi\{f(a+h)\}^2h+\pi\{f(a+2h)\}^2h+\ldots$$

$$+\pi\{f(n+\overline{n-1}\ h)\}^2h]$$

$$=\pi\underset{h\to 0}{\text{Lt}}\ h[(f\{(a)\}^2+\{f(a+h)\}^2+\{f(a+2h)\}^2+\ldots$$

$$+\{f(a+\overline{n-1}h)\}^2]$$

$$=\pi\int_a^b\{f(x)\}^2\ dx=\pi\int_a^b y^2dx.$$

78. Solved Example.

Find the formula for the volume of a hemisphere.

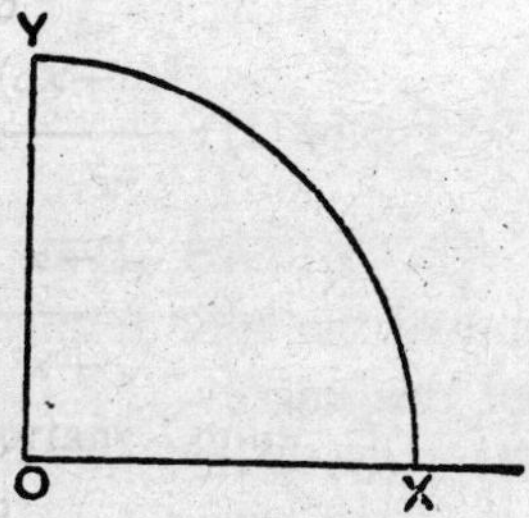

Fig. 15

Let the hemisphere be formed by the revolution of the quadrant XOY of a circle the equation of which is

$$x^2+y^2=a^2.$$

The volume required is

$$\pi\int_0^a y^2dx=\pi\int_0^a (a^2-x^2)dx$$

$$=\pi \underset{h\to 0}{\text{Lt}}\ h\sum_{r=0}^{n-1}(a^2-r^2h^2)$$

$$=\pi \underset{h\to 0}{\text{Lt}}\ h[na^2-h^2\{1^2+2^2+3^2+\ldots+(n-1)^2\}]$$

$$=\pi \underset{h\to 0}{\text{Lt}}\left[nh.\ a^2-h^3\frac{n(n-1)\ (2n-1)}{6}\right]$$

$$=\pi \underset{h\to 0}{\text{Lt}}\left[nh.\ a^2-\frac{nh\ (nh-h)\ (2nh-h)}{6}\right]$$

But here $nh=a$. Hence the volume is

$$\pi \underset{h\to 0}{\text{Lt}} \left[a^3 - \frac{a\ (a-h)\ (2a-h)}{6} \right]$$

$$=\pi\left(a^3-\frac{2a^3}{6}\right)=\tfrac{2}{3}\,\pi a^3$$

EXAMPLES XVIII.

Find the volume of the solid formed by the revolution round the x-axis of the curve

1. $y^2=4ax$ from the vertex to $x=d$.
2. Given in Ex. XVII Q. I.
3. $y=e^{2x}$ from $x=a$ to $x=b$.
4. $y=x$ from $x=0$ to $x=c$.
5. Find the volume of a right circular cone of semi-vertical angle α and height h.

(The cone is formed by the revolution of the triangle given in Ex. XVII Q. 5 round the x-axis).

6. Find the volume of the solid formed by the revolution of the ellipse

$$\frac{x^2}{a^2}+\frac{y^2}{b^2}=1$$

round (1) the major axis, (2) the minor axis.

CHAPTER VI

THE FUNDAMENTAL THEOREM

79. In this article we shall see that yet one more meaning may be attached to the process of integration.

Let $f(x)$ be a function of x which is finite* between given finite values of x. Then, as we have seen above,

$$\int_a^b f(x)\, dx$$

means $\underset{h\to 0}{\text{Lt}}\, h\, [f(a)+f(a+h)+f(a+2h)+\ldots+f(a+\overline{n-1}h)]$,

where $b-a=nh$.

Let $\phi(x)$ be a function such that $f(x)$ is its differential coefficient, *i.e.*, such that

$$f(x)=\phi'(x).$$

Then we shall prove that

$$\int_a^b f(x)\, dx=\phi(b)-\phi(a) \tag{79.1}$$

By definition we have

$$f(a)=\underset{h\to 0}{\text{Lt}}\frac{\phi(a+h)-\phi(a)}{h}.$$

Hence $f(a)=\dfrac{\phi(a+h)-\phi(a)}{h}+\alpha_1$,

---

* $f(x)$ is also supposed to be continuous.

where α_1 is a small quantity which tends to zero as $h \to 0$. Thus

$$h\, f(a) = \phi\,(a+h) - \phi\,(a) + h\,\alpha_1.$$

In the same way we shall have

$$h\, f(a+h) = \phi\,(a+2h) - \phi\,(a+h) + h\,\alpha_2$$

$$h\, f(a+2h) = \phi\,(a+3h) - \phi(a+2h) + h\,\alpha_3$$

....

....

$$h\, f(a+\overline{n-2}h) = \phi\,(a+\overline{n-1}h) - \phi\,(a+\overline{n-2h}) + h\alpha_{n-1},$$

$$h\, f\,(a+\overline{n-1}h) = \phi)a+nh) - \phi\,(a+\overline{n-1}h) + h\alpha_n,$$

where $\alpha_1, \alpha_2 \ldots, \alpha_n$ are quantities such that they all tend to zero when $h \to 0$.

Then by addition,

$$h[f\,(a) + f(a+h) + f(a+2h) + \ldots + f(b-h)]$$

$$= \phi(a+nh) - \phi(a) + h(\alpha_1 + \alpha_2 + \ldots + \alpha_n).$$

If α be the greatest of the quantities $\alpha_1, \alpha_2 \ldots, \alpha_n$, then $h\;(\alpha_1 + \alpha_2 + \ldots + \alpha_n) < nh\alpha$,

$$i.e., < (b-a)\alpha,$$

and therefore tends to zero in the limit. Thus

$$\underset{h \to 0}{\text{Lt}}\, h[f(a) + f(a+h) + f(a+2h) + \ldots + f\,(b-h)]$$

$$= \phi(b) - \phi(a),$$

so that

$$\int^{b} f(x)\, dx = \phi\,(b) - \phi\,(a).$$

This relation remains equally true if we put for the integral the limit

$$\underset{h \to 0}{\text{Lt}}\, h\;\;[f(a) + f(a+h) + f(a+2h) + \ldots + f(b-h) + f(b)],$$

since the additional term $h\, f\,(b)$ vanishes when $h \to 0$.

The equation (79.1) is also written sometimes as

$$\int_a^b f(x)dx = [\phi(x)]_a^b$$

Thus an easier method of finding the value of

$$\int_a^b f(x)dx$$

is to

(1) find out that function $\phi(x)$ whose differential coefficient is $f(x)$,

(2) find the values of $\phi(x)$ when $x=b$ and $x=a$ respectively,

(3) find the excess of $\phi(b)$ over $\phi(a)$.

This will yield the result required.

80. Solved Example.

Evaluate

$$\int_a^b x^8.dx, \int_1^2 3^x dx, \int_0^{\pi/4} \sec^2 x \, dx.$$

By differentiation we have

$$\frac{d}{dx}\left(\frac{x^9}{9}\right) = \frac{1}{9}.\ 9x^8 = x^8.$$

$$\text{Hence } \int_a^b x^8 dx = \left[\frac{x^9}{9}\right]_a^b = \frac{b^9 - a^9}{9}.$$

$$\text{Also, } \frac{d}{dx}\left(\frac{3^x}{\log 3}\right) = \frac{1}{\log 3}.\ 3^x.\ \log 3 = 3^x.$$

Hence $\int_1^2 3^x\,dx = \left[\dfrac{3^x}{\log}\right]_1^2 = \dfrac{3^2-3}{\log 3} = \dfrac{6}{\log 3}$

We know that

$$\frac{d}{dx}(\tan x) = \sec^2 x.$$

Hence $\int_0^{\pi/4} \sec^2 x\,dx = [\tan x]_0^{\pi/4} = 1.$

EXAMPLES XIX

Calculate

1. $\int_2^5 x\,dx.$ 2. $\int_0^1 x^{20}\,dx.$ 3. $\int_1^2 \dfrac{1}{\sqrt{x}}\,dx.$

4. $\int_0^{\pi/2} \cos x\,dx.$ 5. $\int_0^{\pi/2} (-\sin x)\,dx.$

6. $\int_1^2 \dfrac{1}{x}dx.$ 7. $\int_{\pi/4}^{\pi/2} (-\operatorname{cosec}^2 x)dx.$

8. $\displaystyle\int_0^1 \frac{1}{\sqrt{(1-x^2)}}dx.$ 9. $\displaystyle\int_a^b (x-\sin x)\,dx.$

81. Terminology.

The integral on the left-hand side of

$$\int_a^b f(x)\,dx = \phi(b) - \phi(a)$$

is known as a Definite Integral ; b and a are called the Upper and Lower Limits respectively.

We have seen in §74 that b may have any finite value whatever. Thus, replacing b by x we have

$$\int_a^x f(x)\, dx=\phi(x)-\phi(a).$$

This is called a Corrected Integral.

Also, it is not necessary that b should be finite. Let us consider the integral

$$\int_1^\infty \frac{1}{x^2}dx$$

We know that $\dfrac{d}{dx}\left(-\dfrac{1}{x}\right)=\dfrac{1}{x^2}.$

Hence $\displaystyle\int_1^\infty \frac{1}{x^2}dx = \left[-\frac{1}{x}\right]_1^\infty$

Now, the meaning that we attach to $\left[-\dfrac{1}{x}\right]_1^\infty$

is $\displaystyle\operatorname*{Lt}_{b\to\infty}\left[-\frac{1}{x}\right]_1^b$

which $\displaystyle=\operatorname*{Lt}_{b\to\infty}\left(1-\frac{1}{b}\right)=1.$

Hence $\displaystyle\int_1^\infty \frac{1}{x^2}dx=1.$

So, $\int_a^\infty f(x)\,dx$ will always mean

$$\underset{b\to\infty}{Lt} \int_a^b f(x)\,dx, \text{ i.e., } \underset{b\to\infty}{Lt} \left\{\phi(x)\right\}_a^b.$$

Sometimes, in an integral, neither of the two limits is mentioned. Such an integral

$$\int f(x)\,dx$$

is called an Indefinite Integral. It means simply this : Find out that function $\phi(x)$ whose differential coefficient $f(x)$ is.

82. The problem of Differential Calculus was : Given a function, find its differential coefficient. It appears from the foregoing that the problem of Integral Calculus is : Given a function, find that function whose differential coefficient is this given function.

In other words, in Differential Calculus we were given that

$$y=f(x)$$

and we were asked to find a function $f'(x)$ such that

$$\frac{dy}{dx}=f'(x).$$

In Integral Calculus, we are given this latter equation and we are required to find out the function $f(x)$.

Looked at from this point of view Integration may be regarded as the process inverse of Differentiation.

83. Notation.

Thus, regarding integration as the inverse of differentiation we may express the relation

$$\int f(x)\, dx = \phi(x)$$

as
$$\left(\frac{d}{dx}\right)^{-1} f(x) = \phi(x),$$

$$D^{-1} f(x) = \phi(x),$$

or,
$$\frac{1}{D} f(x) = \phi(x).$$

And obviously, $\dfrac{d}{dx} \int f(x)\, dx = f(x)$,

for it is equal to $\dfrac{d}{dx}\,[\phi\,(x)]$, *i.e.*, $\phi'(x)$ or $f(x)$,

so that the effect of putting the sign of differentiation before the integral sign is to yield the original function which was to be integrated.

The integral $\int f(x)\, dx$

is also, for convenience, sometimes written as

$$\int dx\, f(x).$$

84. Solved Examples.

(1) Integrate $\int x^{11}\, dx$, $\int x^{-11}\, dx$, $\int (2x-3)^2\, dx$ and $\int (4-x)^{-3}\, dx$

We have, at once, $\dfrac{d}{dx}\left(\dfrac{x^{12}}{12}\right) = \dfrac{1}{12}.\ 12x^{11} = x^{11}$.

Hence
$$\int x^{11}\, dx = \frac{x^{12}}{12}.$$

$$\text{Again,}\ \frac{d}{dx}\left(\frac{x^{-10}}{-10}\right)=\frac{1}{10}(-10\,x^{-11})=x^{-11}$$

Hence $$\int x^{11}\ dx=-\frac{x^{-10}}{10}.$$

$$\frac{d}{dx}\left\{\frac{(2x-3)^3}{6}\right\}=\frac{1}{6}.\ 3(2x-3)^2.\ 2=(2x-3)^2.$$

Hence $$\int(2x-3)^2\ dx=\frac{1}{6}(2x-3)^3.$$

$$\frac{d}{dx}\left\{\tfrac{1}{2}\ (4-x)^{-2}\right\}=(4-x)^{-3}$$

Hence $$\int(4-x)^{-3}\ dx=\tfrac{1}{2}(4-x)^{-2}$$

(2) Integrate $\displaystyle\int\left(-\frac{1}{1+\sin 2x}\right)dx$

We have

$$\frac{1}{1+\sin 2x}=\frac{1}{\sin^2 x+\cos^2 x+2\sin x\cos x}$$

$$=\frac{1}{(\sin x+\cos x)^2}=\frac{1}{2\sin^2\left(x+\frac{\pi}{4}\right)}.$$

Hence the integral required is

$$\int\left\{-\frac{1}{2\sin^2\left(x+\frac{\pi}{4}\right)}\right\}dx$$

$$\int\left\{-\tfrac{1}{2}\operatorname{cosec}^2\left(x+\frac{\pi}{4}\right)\right\}dx$$

$$=\tfrac{1}{2}\cot\left(x+\frac{\pi}{4}\right).$$

(3) Determine the limit to which the sum of the series

$$\frac{1}{2n}+\frac{1}{2n+1}+\frac{1}{2n+2}+\ldots+\frac{1}{2n+(n-1)}.$$

tends as n increases without limit.

The sum required

$$=\underset{n\to\infty}{\mathrm{Lt}}\ \frac{1}{n}\left[\tfrac{1}{2}+\frac{1}{2+\frac{1}{n}}+\frac{1}{2+\frac{2}{n}}+\ldots+\frac{1}{2+\frac{n-1}{n}}\right]$$

Let $h=\frac{1}{n}$ so that $h\to 0$ as $n\to\infty$. Then the limit becomes

$$\underset{h\to 0}{\mathrm{Lt}}\ h\left[\frac{1}{2}+\frac{1}{2+h}+\frac{1}{2+2h}+\ldots+\frac{1}{2+(n-1)h}\right].$$

But $nh=1$. So, the limit

$$=\int_0^1\frac{dx}{2+x}$$

Now, we know that

$$\log(2+x)=\frac{1}{2+x}.$$

Hence $\displaystyle\int_0^1 \frac{dx}{2+x} = \Big[\log(2+x)\Big]_0^1 = \log 3 - \log 2.$

EXAMPLES XX

Find y when $\dfrac{dy}{dx}$ is

1. e^x 2. $-\dfrac{1}{2\sqrt{x}}$ 3. $(11x+4)^{-3}$ 4. $(2-3x)^{-5}$

5. Integrate $\int a \sin bx\, dx$, $\int a \cos bx\, dx$.

6. At every point (x, y) of a curve, $\dfrac{dy}{dx}=2x^2$. Find the equation to the curve.

7. Integrate $\displaystyle\int \frac{2dx}{1-\sin 2x}$

8. Determine $\displaystyle \underset{n\to\infty}{\text{Lt}} \left[\frac{1}{2n}+\frac{1}{\sqrt{(4n^2-1^2)}}+\frac{1}{\sqrt{(4n^2-2^2)}}+\ldots+\frac{1}{\sqrt{\{4n^2-(n-1)^2\}}}\right]$

9. Prove that

$$\underset{n\to\infty}{\text{Lt}} \left[\frac{1}{n}+\frac{1}{\sqrt{(n^2+n)}}+\frac{1}{\sqrt{(n^2+2n)}}+\ldots+\frac{1}{\sqrt{\{n^2+(n-1)n\}}}\right]=2(\sqrt{2}-1)$$

10. Discuss the statements:

(1) Integration is summation.

(2) Integration is Inverse Differentiation,

and show that if we start with either of them as datum the other will follow as conclusion.

85. Velocity and Acceleration. In Differential Calculus we saw that if the law of motion of a particle was given we could calculate the velocity and acceleration at any time t. Here we are confronted with the reverse problem: Given the velocity or acceleration of a particle at any time t, find the law of motion.

86. Solved Examples.

(1) We shall start with the result of the first part of the solved example under §26 and arrive at the data.

The velocity of a particle at any time t is $21-14t$. Find the law of motion.

We have $\dfrac{ds}{dt}=21-14t$.

$\therefore\ s=\int(21-14t)\,dt$.

The expression whose diff. coff. is $(21-14t)$ is $(21-7t^2)$.

Hence $$s=21t-7t^2.$$

which is the law of motion required.

(2) Prove that if the acceleration of a train is constant the space it describes is proportional to the square of the time of description. (*cf.* §29)

We have

$$\frac{d}{dt}\left(\frac{ds}{dt}\right)\ i.e.,\ \frac{d^2s}{dt^2}=\text{constant}=C,\ \text{say.}$$

Hence $\frac{ds}{dt} = \int C\,dt = Ct.$

Therefore $s = \int Ct\,dt = \frac{1}{2}Ct^2,$

so that $$s \propto t^2.*$$

EXAMPLES XXI

1. The velocity of a particle at any time t is $2t+11$. Find the law of motion.

2. If the velocity of a train at any time t be t^2 ft. per sec., how far does it travel in 5 mins.?

3. Start with the result (acceleration) of Ex. IX, Q. 4 and arrive at the data (law of motion).

4. Show that if the retardation of a particle varies as the reciprocal of the square of the time, the reciprocal of the velocity varies as the time.

5. The acceleration of a particle is given by the expression $a \sin bt$. Find the law of motion.

6. The speed v of a body at time t seconds from start is given by

$$v = t(t-1)(t-2)$$

Show that if the particle moves in a straight line, it returns to its initial position in two seconds.

(Banaras 1946)

---

* The results of these questions are only tentative in character as we have not yet introduced the constant of integration.

CHAPTER VII

FUNDAMENTAL PROPOSITIONS

STANDARD FORMS

87. Fundamental Rules

I. The integral of zero is any constant, for the diff. coeff. of any constant is zero.

Thus, as

$$\frac{d}{dx}(C)=0,$$

therefore, $\int 0\,dx=C$.

II. Any constant may be added to the integral of a function.

Thus, if $\frac{d}{dx}\phi(x)=f(x)$

We have $\frac{d}{dx}\{\phi(x)+C\}=f(x)$.

Hence $\int f(x)dx=\phi(x)+C$,

where C is an arbitrary constant.

This constant may, in particular cases, be determined by additional data, as will be seen in the following solved examples.

Solved Examples.

(1) Find the integral of $\frac{1}{\sqrt{(1-x^2)}}$ which equals 1 when $x=0$.

We have

$$\int \frac{dx}{\sqrt{(1-x^2)}} = \sin^{-1} x + C,$$

where C is an arbitrary constant.

But, when $x=0$, $(\sin^{-1}x+C)=1$.

Therefore, $C=1$.

Hence the integral required is $\sin^{-1}x+1$.

(2) At every point (x, y) of a curve passing through $(1,2)$, $x^2 \frac{dy}{dx} = -1$. Find the equation to the curve.

We have $\frac{dy}{dx} = -\frac{1}{x^2}$

Hence $y = \int \left(-\frac{1}{x^2}\right) dx = \frac{1}{x} + C.$

But the curve passes through the point (1, 2).

Hence $2=1+C$, *i.e.*, $C=1$.

Therefore, the curve required is

$$y = \frac{1}{x} + 1, \quad i.e., \quad xy = x+1.$$

(3) Suppose in Ex. XXI, Q. 1, there is an additional condition that when $t=0$, $s=3$. Find the law of motion.

We have $\frac{ds}{dt} = 2t+11$

Hence $s = \int (2t+11)\, dt = t^2+11t+C.$

But when $t=0$, $s=3$.

Hence $3=0+0+C$ *i.e.*, $C=3$.

Therefore, the law of motion is

$$s=t^2+11t+3.$$

88. Application to Dynamics. Let us deduce the three fundamental equations of Dynamics by the method of Calculus.

Let a particle move in a st. line with initial velocity u and let the constant acceleration be f.

If s be the distance traversed in time t,

$$\frac{d^2s}{dt^2}, \text{ i.e., } \frac{dv}{dt}=f.$$

∴ Integrating, $v=ft+C$.

But $v=u$, when $t=0$, ∴ $C=u$.

Hence $v=u+ft$. (88.1)

Now, from (88.1),

$$\frac{ds}{dt}=u+ft.$$

∴ Integrating again,

$s=ut+\frac{1}{2}ft^2+A$.

But $s=0$, when $t=0$. ∴ $A=0$.

Hence $s=ut+\frac{1}{2}ft^2$. (88.2)

Lastly,

$$f=\frac{dv}{dt}=\frac{dv}{ds}\cdot\frac{ds}{dt}=v\frac{dv}{ds}$$

Hence, integrating with respect to s,

$\frac{1}{2}v^2=fs+B$.

But $v=u$ when $s=0$.

$\therefore v^2=u^2+2fs$. (88.3)

EXAMPLES XXII

1. Find y, given that $\frac{dy}{dx}=\sec^2 x$ and $y=1$ when $x=0$.

2. Find the integral of $\sin x$ which vanishes when $x=0$.

3. Find the curve passing through (0, 2) at every point (x,y) of which $e^x \frac{dy}{dx}+3=0$.

4. The velocity of a particle at any instant t is $2at+b$. Find the law of motion, given that $s=c$, when $t=0$.

5. The acceleration of a particle at any time t is $\frac{2}{t^3}$. Find the law of motion, given that when $t=1$, $v=2$ and $s=4$.

6. Show that in Ex. XXI, Q. 3, the result remains unaffected if we impose the additional condition that $s=v=0$ when $t=0$, *i.e.*, t, s, v vanish together.

89. Henceforth we shall express the constant of integration only where necessary.

Integration of x^n. $(n \neq -1)$

We have immediately, $\frac{d}{dx}\left(\frac{x^{n+1}}{n+1}\right)=x^n$.

Hence, $\int x^n dx=\frac{x^{n+1}}{n+1}$.

Thus $\int x^7\, dx=\frac{x^8}{8}$ and $\int x^{-3/4}dx=4x^{1/4}$

90. Integrate $1/x$

We know that $\dfrac{d}{dx}\left(\log x\right)=\dfrac{1}{x}$

Hence $\displaystyle\int\frac{dx}{x}=\log x.$

This seems to be an apparent exception to the above rule. But, in reality it is not so. We have

$$\int x^n\,dx=\frac{x^{n+1}}{n+1}+\text{C}.$$

where C is an arbitrary constant. Then

$$\int x^n dx=\left(\frac{x^{n+1}}{n+1}-\frac{1}{n+1}\right)+\left(\text{C}+\frac{1}{n+1}\right)$$

$$=\frac{{}^{n+1}-1}{n+1}+\text{K},$$

where $\text{K}=\text{C}+\dfrac{1}{n+1}$ and is thus still an arbitrary constant.

Taking the limit, we have,

$$\underset{n\to-1}{\text{Lt}}\int x^n dx=\underset{n\to-1}{\text{Lt}}\ \frac{x^{n+1}-1}{n+1}+\text{K}.$$

$$=\underset{a\to0}{\text{Lt}}\frac{x^a-1}{a}+\text{K}.$$

$$=\log x+\text{K}. \qquad (\S\ 8)$$

Hence, $\displaystyle\int\frac{dx}{x}=\log x+\text{K},$

where the integral contains a negative infinite portion

$-\dfrac{1}{n+1}$ and an arbitrary constant K.

91. We have immediately,

$$\frac{d}{dx}\left\{\frac{(ax+b)^{n+1}}{(n+1)a}\right\}=(ax+b)^n,$$

and $$\frac{d}{dx}\left\{\frac{\log (ax+b)}{a}\right\}=\frac{1}{ax+b},$$

Hence, $$\int (ax+b)^n dx = \frac{(ax+b)^{n+1}}{(n+1)a}$$

and $$\int \frac{dx}{ax+b} = \frac{1}{a}\log (ax+b).$$

92. Solved Examples.

(1) $$\int (2x-3)^4 dx=\frac{(2x-3)^5}{5.2}=\frac{1}{10}(2x-3)^5$$

$$\int (4-3x)^{-2/3}\ dx= \frac{(4-3x)^{1/3}}{\frac{1}{3}(-3)} = -\ (4-3x)^{1/3}$$

(2) $$\int \frac{dx}{20x-13}=\frac{1}{20}\log (20x-13),$$

$$\int \frac{dx}{4-5x}=-\ \tfrac{1}{5}\log (4-5x).$$

93. Sometimes we come across expressions of the forms

$$\{f(x)\}^n f'(x) \text{ and } \frac{f'(x)}{f(x)}$$

for integration. We have immediately,

$$\frac{d}{dx}\left[\frac{1}{n+1}\{f(x)\}^{n+1}\right]=\{f(x)\}^n f'(x)$$

and $$\frac{d}{dx}\log f(x) = \frac{f'(x)}{f(x)}$$

Hence $$\int \{f(x)\}^n f'(x)\, dx = \frac{1}{n+1}\{f(x)\}^{n+1}$$

and $$\int \frac{f'(x)}{f(x)}dx=\log f(x).$$

The second of these results which is very important, may be expressed thus : The integral of a fraction of which the numerator is the differential coefficient of the denominator is log (*denominator*).

94. Solved Examples.

(1) $$\int \frac{2dx}{2x+5}=\log(2x+5).$$

$$\int \frac{(4x-3)dx}{2x^2-3x+5} = \log(2x^2-3x+5)$$ (Banaras 1951)

(2) $$\int (5x^2-3x+2)^3(10x-3)dx=\tfrac{1}{4} (5x^2-3x+2)^4$$

$$\int (\log x+2) \frac{dx}{x}=\tfrac{1}{2} (\log x+2)^2.$$

(3) $$\int \cot x\, dx = \int \frac{\cos x}{\sin x}dx= \log \sin x.$$

$$\int \tan x\, dx=\int \frac{\sec x \tan x}{\sec x}dx=\log \sec x.$$

EXAMPLES XXIII

Write down the integrals of

1. x^{243}, $x^{-11/3}$, x^c.

2. $(15x-2)^{11/2}$, $(2-15x)^{11/2}$, $(15x-2)^{-11/2}$
$(2-15x)^{-11/2}$, $(a-bx)^n$.

3. $\dfrac{1}{b-ax}$, $\dfrac{1}{a-bx}$, $\dfrac{1}{(5x+2)^{3/2}}$.

4. $(e^x+\log x)^{3/2}\{e^x+\dfrac{1}{x}\}$, $(ax^2+bx+c)^n\,(2ax+b)$,
$-(c-bx-ax^2)^n\,(2ax+b)$.

5. $\dfrac{2ax+b}{ax^2+bx+c}$, $\dfrac{1}{x}$, $\dfrac{1}{x\log x}$, $\dfrac{2x+3}{(x^2+3x-2)^{3/2}}$

6. $\dfrac{e^x-e^{-x}}{e^x+e^{-x}}$, $\dfrac{1}{\sqrt{(1-x^2)}\,\sin^{-1}x}$, $\dfrac{-1}{\sin x\cos x}$.

7. $\sin^{-4}x\cos x$ (Banaras 1943).

8. Evaluate $\displaystyle\int_0^1 \frac{x\,dx}{\sqrt{(1+x^2)}}$ (Banaras 1945, 1951).

9. Integrate
$\int(5x^2-10x+17)^2\,(x-1)\,dx$ (Banaras 1946, 1955).

95. Standard Forms. The following Standard Forms may now be committed to memory:

$$\int x^n dx=\frac{x^{n+1}}{n+1},\ (n\neq-1).$$

$$\int \frac{dx}{x} = \log x. \quad \int a^x dx = \frac{a^x}{\log a}.$$

$$\int e^x dx = e^x. \quad \int e^{ax} dx = \frac{1}{a} e^{ax}$$

$$\int \cos x \, dx = \sin x. \quad \int \sin x \, dx = - \cos x.$$

$$\int \sec^2 x \, dx = \tan x.$$

$$\int \operatorname{cosec}^2 x \, dx = -\cot x.$$

$$\int \sec x \tan x \, dx = \sec x.$$

$$\int \operatorname{cosec} x \cot x \, dx = -\operatorname{cosec} x.$$

$$\int \tan x \, dx = \log \sec x.$$

$$\int \cot x \, dx = \log \sin x.$$

$$\int \frac{dx}{\sqrt{(a^2 - x^2)}} = \sin^{-1} \frac{x}{a} \text{ or } - \cos^{-1} \frac{x}{a}.$$

$$\int \frac{dx}{x^2 + a^2} = \frac{1}{a} \tan^{-1} \frac{x}{a} \text{ or } - \frac{1}{a} \cot^{-1} \frac{x}{a}.$$

$$\int \frac{dx}{x\sqrt{(x^2 - a^2)}} = \frac{1}{a} \sec^{-1} \frac{x}{a} \text{ or } - \frac{1}{a} \operatorname{cosec}^{-1} \frac{x}{a}.$$

$$\int \frac{dx}{\sqrt{(2ax - x^2)}} = \operatorname{vers}^{-1} \frac{x}{a} \text{ or } - \operatorname{covers}^{-1} \frac{x}{a}.$$

96. Fundamental Rules (Contd.)

III $$\int cu \, dx = c \int u \, dx,$$

where c is a constant and u is a function of x.

Let $\dfrac{dv}{dx}=u,$

so that $v=\int u\,dx.$

We have $\dfrac{d}{dx}(cv)=c\dfrac{dv}{dx}=cu.$

Hence $cv=\int cu\,dx,$

i.e., $c\int u\,dx=\int cu\,dx,$

so that the operation of integration is commutative with regard to constants.

IV. $\int(u+v+w+...)dx=\int u\,dx+\int v\,dx+\int w\,dx+...$

We have

$$\frac{d}{dx}[\int u\,dx+\int v dx+...]=u+v+...$$

Hence $\int(u+v+w+...)dx=\int u\,dx+\int v\,dx+\int w\,dx+...$
so that the operation of integration is distributive.

97. Solved Examples.

(1) $\int(2x^2-6x+3)dx=\int 2x^2dx-\int 6xdx+\int 3dx$

$=2\int x^2dx-6\int xdx+3\int dx=\frac{2}{3}x^3-3x^2+3.$

(2) $\displaystyle\int\frac{x+2}{x+8}dx=\int\left[1+\left(\frac{x+2}{x+8}-1\right)\right]dx$

$\displaystyle=\int dx-6\int\frac{dx}{x+8}=x-6\log(x+8).$

(3) $\displaystyle\int\sin^2\theta\,d\theta=\int\frac{1-\cos 2\theta}{2}d\theta$

$=\frac{1}{2}\int d\theta-\frac{1}{2}\int\cos 2\theta\,d\theta$

$=\frac{1}{2}\theta-\frac{1}{4}\sin 2\theta=\frac{1}{2}(\theta-\sin\theta\cos\theta).$

EXAMPLES XXIV

Write down the integrals of

1. $x+e^x$, $x^2-\frac{1}{x}$, $ax+\frac{b}{x^2}$, ax^2+bx+c.

2. $\cos^2 x$, $\sin^3 x$, $\sin x \cos x$, $\sin mx \sin nx$.

3. $\sin^n x \cos x$, $\tan^4 x \sec^2 x$, $\frac{\operatorname{cosec}^{-1} x}{x\sqrt{(x^2-1)}}$.

4. $\frac{x}{x+a}$, $\frac{x+a}{x}$, $\frac{x}{a-x}$, $\frac{a-x}{x}$.

5. $\frac{ax^2+bx+c}{x^4}$, $\frac{c-bx-ax^2}{x^3}$, $\frac{1}{x^2-6x+13}$,

$\frac{1}{4x^2-4x+5}$.

6. $\frac{e^x}{e^x+11}$, $\frac{1}{\cot x \log \sec x}$, 4^x+x^3.

7. $\frac{1}{x\sqrt{(x^2-121)}}$, $\frac{1}{\sqrt{(6x-x^2)}}$.

8. Evaluate $\int_0^{\pi/2} \sin^2 x \, dx$ (Banaras 1944)

9. Evaluate $\int_0^{\pi/2} \sin^3\theta \, d\theta$.

CHAPTER VIII

METHOD OF SUBSTITUTION

98. The Main Theorem.

$$\int f(x)\,dx = \int f(x)\frac{dx}{dt}dt,$$

where x is a function of t.

By means of this formula we can change the variable x into another variable t and thus throw the expression to be integrated into a form which may be easier for integration.

Let $y = \int f(x)dx$,

so that $\frac{dy}{dx} = f(x)$.

As y is a function of x and x is a function of t, y is also a function of t. Hence

$$\frac{dy}{dt} = \frac{dy}{dx}\cdot\frac{dx}{dt} = f(x)\frac{dx}{dt}.$$

$$\therefore y = \int f(x)\frac{dx}{dt}dt,$$

$$\text{i.e., } \int f(x)\,dx = \int f(x)\frac{dx}{dt}\,dt.$$

This is the most powerful method of integration. All that we are to do in a particular case is to replace dx

by $\frac{dx}{dt} dt$ and express $f(x)$ in terms of t. Its use will be manifest from the following solved examples.

99. Solved Examples.

(1) Integrate $\int \frac{\sin\sqrt{x}}{\sqrt{x}} dx$ (Banaras 1952).

Let $x = t^2$,

so that $dx = \frac{dx}{dt} dt = 2t\, dt$

$$\therefore \int \frac{\sin\sqrt{x}}{\sqrt{x}} dx = \int \frac{\sin t}{t} 2t\, dt.$$

$= 2\int \sin t\, dt = -2\cos t = -2\cos\sqrt{x}.$

(2) Evaluate $\int_2^3 \frac{x\, dx}{1+x^2}$.

First Method $\int_2^3 \frac{x\, dx}{1+x^2} = \frac{1}{2} \int_2^3 \frac{2x\, dx}{1+x^2}$

$$= \frac{1}{2} \left[\log(1+x^2)\right]_2^3 = \frac{1}{2}[\log 10 - \log 5] = \frac{1}{2} \log 2.$$

Second Method. Let $x = \tan\theta$,

so that $dx = \sec^2\theta d\theta$.

Then the integral $= \int_{x=2}^{x=3} \frac{\tan\theta . \sec^2\theta d\theta}{1+\tan^2\theta}$

$$= \int_{x=2}^{x=3} \tan\theta \, d\theta = \Big[\log \sec\theta\Big]_{x=2}^{x=3}$$

Now, $\tan\theta = x$.

Therefore,

$$\sec\theta = \sqrt{(1+x^2)}$$

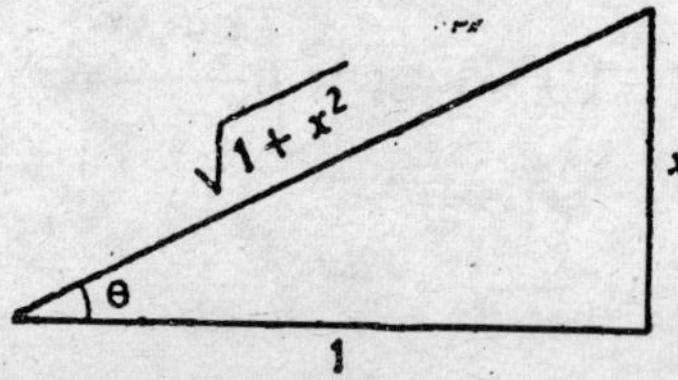

Fig. 16

So, the integral $= \Big[\log\sqrt{(1+x^2)}\Big]_2^3$

$$= \log\sqrt{10} - \log\sqrt{5} = \tfrac{1}{2}\log 10 - \tfrac{1}{2}\log 5 = \tfrac{1}{2}\log 2.$$

(3) **Evaluate** $\int_0^{\pi/2} \sin^2 x \cos^3 x \, dx.$

(Banaras 1941, 1944, 1946, 1952, 1956, 1957.)

Put $\sin x = t$,

so that $\cos x \dfrac{dx}{dt} = 1$, *i.e.*, $dx = \dfrac{1}{\cos x} dt.$

Now, when $x=0$, $t=0$,
and when $x=\pi/2$, $t=1$.

Hence, $\int_0^{\pi/2} \sin^2 x \cos^3 x \, dx = \int_0^1 \sin^2 x \cos^2 x \, dt$

$$= \int_0^1 t^2(1-t^2)\,dt = \int_0^1 t^2\,dt - \int_0^1 t^4\,dt$$

$$= \left[\tfrac{1}{3}t^3 - \tfrac{1}{5}t^5\right]_0^1 = \tfrac{1}{3} - \tfrac{1}{5} = \tfrac{2}{15}$$

(4) **Evaluate** $\displaystyle\int_1^5 \frac{dt}{\sqrt{(15+2t-t^2)}}$ (Banaras 1946)

The expression under the radical sign

$$=15-(t^2-2t)=16-(t-1)^2.$$

Hence, let us put $t=1+x$

and $dt=dx$.

When $t=1,\ x=0$;

when $t=5,\ x=4$.

Therefore, $\displaystyle\int_1^5 \frac{dt}{\sqrt{(15+2t-t^2)}}$

$$= \int_1^5 \frac{dt}{\sqrt{[16-(t-1)^2]}} = \int_0^4 \frac{dx}{\sqrt{(16-x^2)}}$$

$$= \left(\sin^{-1}\tfrac{1}{4}x\right)_0^4 = \frac{\pi}{2}$$

EXAMPLES XXV

Integrate :—

1. $ae^x \cos(e^x)$, $\dfrac{e^{\tan^{-1}x}}{1+x^2}$. (Banaras 1941), $\dfrac{x^2}{1+x^6}$. (1954)

2. $\dfrac{1}{(1+x)\sqrt{(1-x^2)}}$. (Put $x=\cos\theta$).

3. Evaluate $\int_0^{\pi/2} \sin^2 x \cos x \, dx$. (1954)

4. Evaluate $\displaystyle\int_1^e \frac{(\log x)^3}{x} dx$.

5. Evaluate $\displaystyle\int_{-1}^{0} \frac{dt}{\sqrt{(-t^2-2t)}}$. (Put $t=x-1$).

6. Evaluate $\displaystyle\int_3^{2+\sqrt{2}} \frac{dx}{(x-2)\sqrt{(x^2-4x+3)}}$

100. It will be easily seen that all the four forms of §§ 91, 93 can be derived from the above theorem as particular cases. For example, let us consider

$$\int(ax+b)^n dx \quad \text{and} \quad \int \frac{f'(x)}{f(x)} dx.$$

In the first, put $ax+b=u$.

Then $\qquad dx=\frac{1}{a}du.$

$$\therefore \int (ax+b)^n dx = \frac{1}{a} \int u^n du = \frac{1}{a} \cdot \frac{u^{n+1}}{n+1}$$

$$= \frac{1}{a} \cdot \frac{(ax+b)^{n+1}}{n+1}$$

In the second, put $f(x)=t$.

Differentiating logarithmically, we have

$$\log f(x) = \log t.$$

$$\therefore \frac{f'(x)}{f(x)} dx = \frac{dt}{t}$$

Hence, $\displaystyle \int \frac{f'(x)}{f(x)} dx = \int \frac{dt}{t}$

$$= \log t = \log f(x).$$

We leave the other two forms as an exercise for the student.

101. Integral of cosec x.

Let $\qquad \tan\frac{x}{2}=t.$

Then, $\qquad \log \tan\frac{x}{2} = \log t.$

Therefore $\dfrac{1}{2} \cdot \dfrac{1}{\tan \dfrac{x}{2}} \sec^2 \dfrac{x}{2} dx = \dfrac{dt}{t}$

i.e., $\dfrac{dx}{2 \sin \dfrac{x}{2} \cos \dfrac{x}{2}}$, or, $\dfrac{dx}{\sin x} = \dfrac{dt}{t}$

Hence, $\int \operatorname{cosec} x \, dx = \int \dfrac{dt}{t} = \log t = \log \tan \dfrac{x}{2}$

$$= -\log (\operatorname{cosec} x + \cot x)$$

102. To integrate $\int \sec x \, dx$, (1960)

put $x = y - \dfrac{\pi}{2}$,

so that $dx = dy$.

Then, $\int \sec x \, dx = \int \sec \left(y - \dfrac{\pi}{2} \right) dy$

$= \int \operatorname{cosec} y \, dy = \log \tan \dfrac{y}{2} = \log \tan \left(\dfrac{\pi}{4} + \dfrac{x}{2} \right)$

$$= \log (\sec x + \tan x).$$

103. Integral of $\dfrac{1}{\sqrt{(x^2+a^2)}}$ (Banaras 1951)

To find $\int \dfrac{dx}{\sqrt{(x^2+a^2)}}$.

put $x = a \tan \theta$,

so that

$dx = a \sec^2\theta \, d\theta$.

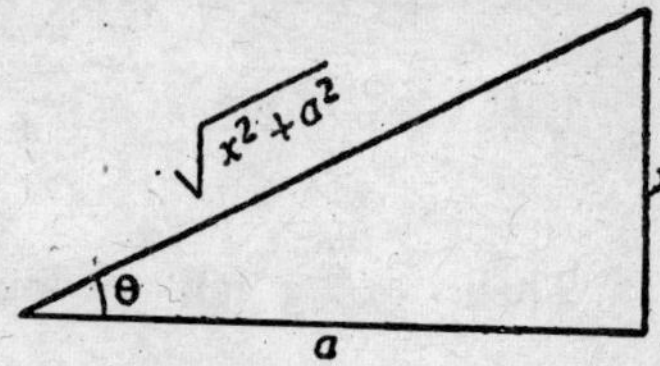

Fig. 17

Then $\int \frac{dx}{\sqrt{(x^2+a^2)}} = \int \sec\theta \, d\theta$

$= \log(\sec\theta + \tan\theta) = \log \frac{x+\sqrt{(x^2+a^2)}}{a}$

104. Integral of $\frac{1}{\sqrt{(x^2-a^2)}}$ (Banaras 1952)

To integrate $\int \frac{dx}{\sqrt{(x^2-a^2)}}$ put $x=a\sec\theta$,

so that $dx=a\sec\theta\tan\theta\,d\theta$. Then,

$$\int \frac{dx}{\sqrt{(x^2-a^2)}} = \int \frac{a\sec\theta\tan\theta\,d\theta}{a\tan\theta} = \int \sec\theta\,d\theta$$

$= \log(\sec\theta+\tan\theta)$

$= \log \frac{x+\sqrt{(x^2-a^2)}}{a}$

105. To integrate $\sqrt{(a^2-x^2)}$. (Banaras 1951)

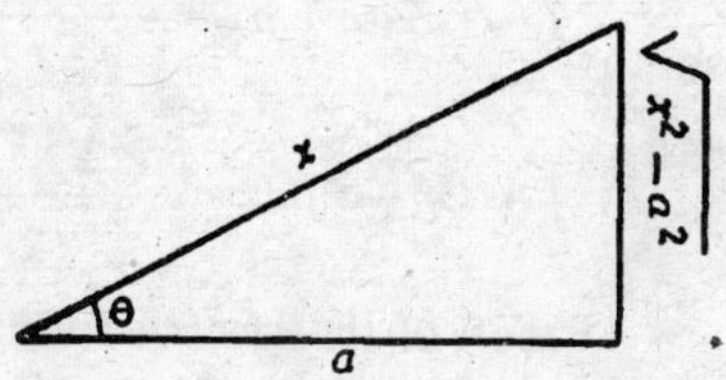

Fig. 18

Let $x=a\sin\theta$.

Then $dx=a\cos\theta\,d\theta$

Hence $\int \sqrt{(a^2-x^2)}\,dx = a^2 \int \cos^2\theta\,d\theta = a^2 \int \frac{1+\cos 2\theta}{2} d\theta$

$$= \frac{a^2}{4}\sin 2\theta + \frac{a^2}{2}\theta = \frac{1}{2}a^2\sin\theta\cos\theta + \frac{a^2}{2}\theta$$

$$=\frac{x(\sqrt{a^2-x^2})}{2}+\frac{a^2}{2}\sin^{-1}\frac{x}{a}$$

106. Additional Standard Forms

$$\int\frac{dx}{\sqrt{(x^2+a^2)}}=\log\left[x+\sqrt{(x^2+a^2)}\right]$$

$$\int\frac{dx}{\sqrt{(x^2-a^2)}}=\log\left[x+\sqrt{(x^2-a^2)}\right]$$

$$\int\sqrt{(a^2-x^2)}\,dx=\frac{x(\sqrt{a^2-x^2})}{2}+\frac{a^2}{2}\sin^{-1}\frac{x}{a}.$$

$$\int\sqrt{(x^2+a^2)}\,dx=\frac{x\sqrt{(x^2+a^2)}}{2}+\frac{a^2}{2}\log\left[x+\sqrt{(x^2+a^2)}\right]$$

$$\int\sqrt{(x^2-a^2)}\,dx=\frac{x\sqrt{(x^2-a^2)}}{2}-\frac{a^2}{2}\log\left[x+\sqrt{(x^2-a^2)}\right].$$

Proofs of the last two formulae will be given in the next chapter.

Compare the first two of the above formulae with the following formula of § 95 :—

$$\int\frac{dx}{\sqrt{(a^2-x^2)}}=\sin^{-1}\frac{x}{a}\text{ or, }-\cos^{-1}\frac{x}{a}$$

107. Solved Examples.

(1) Integrate $\dfrac{1}{\sqrt{(x^2-6x+10)}}$; $\sqrt{(x^2-4x+13)}$.

We have

$$\int \frac{dx}{\sqrt{[(x-3)^2+1]}} - \int \frac{dy}{\sqrt{(y^2+1)}}, \text{ where } y=x-3.$$

Hence the integral

$=\log [y+\sqrt{(y^2+1)}] =\log \{x-3+\sqrt{[(x-3)^2+1]}\}$

$=\log [(x-3)+\sqrt{(x^2-6x+10)}]$.

$\int \sqrt{(x^2-4x+13)}dx = \int \sqrt{\{(x-2)^2+9\}}dx$

$= \int\sqrt{(y^2+9)}\ dy$, where $y=x-2$.

Hence the integral reqd.

$$= \frac{y\sqrt{(y^2+9)}}{2} + \frac{9}{2}\log [y+\sqrt{(y^2+9)}]$$

$$= \frac{(x-2)\sqrt{(x^2-4x+13)}}{2} + \frac{9}{2}\log [x-2+\sqrt{(x^2-4x+13)}]$$

(2) $\int \sqrt{\left[\frac{a-x}{a+x}\right]}dx = \int \frac{a-x}{\sqrt{(a^2-x^2)}}dx$

$$=a \int \frac{dx}{\sqrt{(a^2-x^2)}} - \int \frac{x\,dx}{\sqrt{(a^2-x^2)}}$$

$$=a \int \frac{dx}{\sqrt{(a^2-x^2)}} + \tfrac{1}{2} \int \frac{-2x\,dx}{\sqrt{(a^2-x^2)}}$$

$$=a \sin^{-1} \frac{x}{a} + \sqrt{(a^2-x^2)}.$$

(3) Evaluate $\int_0^{\pi/4} \sec^3 x\ dx$ (Banaras 1946)

Putting $\tan x=t$, so that $\sec^2 x\, dx=dt$, we have

$$\int \sec^3 x\, dx=\int \sqrt{(1+t^2)}\ dt$$

$$=\frac{t\sqrt{(1+t^2)}}{2}+\log\ [t+\sqrt{(1+t^2)}\ ]$$

$$=\tfrac{1}{2}\tan x\sec x+\tfrac{1}{2}\log\ (\tan x+\sec x)$$

$$\therefore \int_0^{\pi/4} \sec^3 x\ dx$$

$$=\tfrac{1}{2}\Big[\tan x\ \sec x+\log\ (\tan x+\sec x)\Big]_0^{\pi/4}$$

$$=\tfrac{1}{2}\ \{\sqrt{2}+\log(\sqrt{2}+1)\}.$$

(4) Evaluate $\displaystyle\int_2^3 \frac{x\,dx}{\sqrt{(1+x)}}$ (Banaras 1950)

First Method.

$$\int \frac{x\,dx}{\sqrt{(1+x)}}=\int\frac{(1+x)-1}{\sqrt{(1+x)}}\,dx$$

$$=\int\sqrt{(1+x)}\ dx-\int\frac{dx}{\sqrt{(1+x)}}=\tfrac{2}{3}(1+x)^{3/2}-2\sqrt{(1+x)}$$

$$=\tfrac{2}{3}(x-2)\sqrt{(x+1)}.$$

$$\therefore \int\frac{x\,dx}{\sqrt{(1+x)}}=\tfrac{2}{3}\ \Big[(x-2)\sqrt{(x+1)}\ \Big]_2^3=\tfrac{4}{3}$$

Second Method.

Let $\sqrt{(1+x)}=y$.

Then $$\frac{dx}{2\sqrt{(1+x)}}=dy.$$

Hence, $$\int \frac{x\,dx}{\sqrt{(1+x)}}=2\int x\,dy=2\int (y^2-1)\,dy$$

$$=\tfrac{2}{3}y^3-2y.$$

Now, when $x=2$, $y=\sqrt{3}$,
and when $x=3$, $y=2$.

Hence $$\int_2^3 \frac{x\,dx}{\sqrt{(1+x)}}=\tfrac{2}{3}\Big[y^3-3y\Big]_{\sqrt{3}}^{2}=\tfrac{4}{3}$$

EXAMPLES XXVI

Integrate,

1. $\sec ax$, $\operatorname{cosec} ax$.
2. $\cot^7 x \operatorname{cosec}^2 x$, $\tan^6 x \sec^2 x$
3. $\dfrac{1}{\sqrt{(x^2-4)}}$, $\dfrac{1}{\sqrt{(4-x^2)}}$, $\dfrac{1}{\sqrt{(x^2+4)}}$, $\sqrt{(x^2+4)}$, $\sqrt{(x^2-4)}$, $\sqrt{(4-x^2)}$.
4. $\dfrac{1}{\sqrt{(x^2-4x+5)}}$, $\sqrt{(x^2-4x+5)}$, $\dfrac{1}{\sqrt{(7+6x-x^2)}}$, $\sqrt{(7+6x-x^2)}$.
5. Evaluate $\int_0^a x\sqrt{(a^2-x^2)}\,dx$. (Banaras 1949, 1955)

Integrate,

6. $\dfrac{1}{\sin^2 x \cos^2 x}$ (put $\cot x = u$). (Banaras 1946), $\dfrac{\cos x}{a+b \sin x}$ (1956).

7. $x\left(3x^2-2a^2\right)^p$, $\dfrac{1-\cos x}{x-\sin x}$, $\dfrac{1+x}{x+3e^{-x}}$,

8. $\dfrac{1}{\sqrt{(2x+1)}}$, $\dfrac{2x-1}{\sqrt{(2x+1)}}$, $\sqrt{\left[\dfrac{2x-1}{2x+1}\right]}$

9. $\dfrac{1}{\sin x-\cos x}$, $\dfrac{1}{a \cos x+b \sin x}$. (Banaras 1946)

10. $\tan^2 x$, $\tan^3 x$, $\tan^4 x$, $\tan^3 x \sec x$.

11. $\dfrac{1}{x \log x}$, $\dfrac{1}{x \log x \log (\log x)}$. 12. $\dfrac{2+e^x}{1+e^x}$

Evaluate

13. $\displaystyle\int_0^2 \frac{dx}{(4+3x^2)^{3/2}}$. 14. $\displaystyle\int_0^{\pi/4} \frac{\sin\theta}{\cos^2 \theta}\, d\theta$.

15. (*i*) $\displaystyle\int_0^{\sqrt{2}} \frac{dx}{\sqrt{(2-x^2)}}$. (*ii*) $\displaystyle\int_{\pi/4}^{\pi/2} \frac{\cos x}{\sin^2 x}\, dx$

(*iii*) $\displaystyle\int_0^{\pi/4} \sec^2 \theta \, d\theta$. (Banaras 1940)

CHAPTER IX

INTEGRATION BY PARTS

108. The Main Theorem.

Suppose we are required to integrate the product uv of two functions u and v of x. Sometimes it so happens that one of the two functions is easily integrable while the other is not. This device, known as "Integration by Parts" is employed in such cases.

In the particular case under consideration, let v be the function easily integrable and let V be its integral so that

$$V=\int v\,dx, \qquad i.e., \quad \frac{dV}{dx}=v.$$

Now, $$\frac{d}{dx}(uV)=u\frac{dV}{dx}+V\frac{du}{dx}$$

$$=uv+V\frac{du}{dx}.$$

Integrating both the sides we have

$$uV=\int uv\,dx+\int V\frac{du}{dx}dx,$$

so that $$\int uv\,dx=vV-\int V\frac{du}{dx}dx.$$

Expressed in words, the formula runs :—

Integral of Product=1st function×Integral of 2nd—Integral of {Diff. coeff. of 1st×Integral of 2nd.}

109. Solved Examples.

(i) Integrate $x \cos bx$ and $x^2 \sin bx$.

We know that the integral of $\cos bx$ is $\dfrac{1}{b}\sin bx$.

Hence, treating x as the first and $\cos bx$ as the second function, we have

$$\int x \cos bx\, dx = \frac{x \sin bx}{b} - \int 1 . \frac{\sin bx}{b} dx$$

$$= \frac{x \sin bx}{b} - \frac{1}{b}\left(-\frac{\cos bx}{b}\right)$$

$$= \frac{x \sin bx}{b} + \frac{\cos bx}{b^2}.$$

And $$\int x^2 \sin bx\, dx = x^2\left(-\frac{\cos bx}{b}\right)$$

$$-\int 2x\left(-\frac{\cos bx}{b}\right) dx$$

$$= -\frac{x^2 \cos bx}{b} + \frac{2}{b}\int x \cos bx\, dx$$

$$= -\frac{x^2 \cos bx}{b} + \frac{2}{b}\left(\frac{x \sin bx}{b} + \frac{\cos bx}{b^2}\right)$$

$$= -\frac{x^2 \cos bx}{b} + \frac{2x \sin bx}{b^2} + \frac{2 \cos bx}{b^3}.$$

(2) The operation of integrating by parts may be repeated several times.

$$\int x^2 e^x dx = x^2 e^x - \int 2x e^x dx.$$
$$= x^2 e^x - 2 \int x e^x dx.$$
$$= x^2 e^x - 2\{x e^x - \int 1. e^x dx\}$$
$$= x^2 e^x - 2 \{x e^x - e^x\}$$
$$= (x^2 - 2x + 2)e^x.$$

(3) Sometimes unity may advisedly be taken as one of the two functions.

$$\int \sin^{-1} x \ dx = \int 1. \ \sin^{-1} x \, dx$$
$$= x \sin^{-1} x - \int x. \frac{1}{\sqrt{(1-x^2)}} dx$$
$$= x \sin^{-1} x + \sqrt{(1-x^2)}$$

(4) Integrate $\sqrt{(x^2+a^2)}$ by parts.

$$\int \sqrt{(x^2+a^2)} dx = x\sqrt{(x^2+a^2)} - \int x \frac{d}{dx}\{\sqrt{(x^2+a^2)}\} dx$$
$$= x\sqrt{(x^2+a^2)} - \int \frac{x^2}{\sqrt{(x^2+a^2)}} dx$$
$$= x\sqrt{(x^2+a^2)} - \int \frac{(x^2+a^2-a^2)}{\sqrt{(x^2+a^2)}} dx$$

so that $\int \sqrt{(x^2+a^2)} dx = x\sqrt{(x^2+a^2)}$

$$-\int \sqrt{(x^2+a^2)} \, dx + a^2 \int \frac{dx}{\sqrt{(x^2+a^2)}}.$$

Transposing and dividing by 2.

$$\int\sqrt{(x^2+a^2)}dx=\frac{x\sqrt{(x^2+a^2)}}{2}+\frac{a^2}{2}\log\left[x+\sqrt{(x^2+a^2)}\right]$$

EXAMPLES XXVII

Integrate

1. $x \sin x$, $x^2 \cos x$, $x \sin^2 x$, $x^2 \sin^2 2x$.

2. $x^2 e^{2x}$ (1955), $x^3 e^x$, $x^3 e^{3x}$, $x^3 e^{2x}$

3. $\log x$, (1957) (Banaras 1940)
   $x \log x$, (1958), $x^2\log x$, $x^n \log x$.

4. $\sin x \sin 2x$, $x^2 \sin x$ (1957), $x \sin x \sin 3x$.

5. $\tan^{-1}x$. (Banaras 1942), $x \tan^{-1}x$, $\sin^{-1}x$, $x^2\sin^{-1}x$ (1956).

6. Evaluate $\int_0^{\pi/2} x \sin x\, dx$, $\int_0^{\pi/4} x \cos x\, dx$ (Banaras 1943, 1958)

and $\int_0^{\pi} x \sin x\, dx$ (Banaras 1945)

7. Evaluate $\int_0^{\infty} xe^{-x}\, dx$ and $\int_0^{\infty} x^2e^{-x}\, dx$. $(e^{-\infty}=0)$

8. Integrate $\sqrt{(a^2-x^2)}$ and $\sqrt{(x^2-a^2)}$ by parts.

9. Integrate $\int\frac{\log x}{x}dx$ by parts. (Banaras 1942)

110. We added a few more solved examples.

(1) Integrate $\dfrac{xe^x}{(1+x)^2}$ (1955)

We have $\displaystyle\int \frac{xe^x}{(1+x)^2}dx = \int \frac{(1+x)-1}{(1+x)^2}e^x dx$

$$=\int \frac{e^x\,dx}{1+x} - \int \frac{e^x\,dx}{(1+x)^2}$$

$$=\int \frac{e^x\,dx}{1+x} - \left\{ -\frac{e^x}{1+x} + \int \frac{e^x dx}{1+x} \right\} = \frac{e^x}{1+x}$$

(2) Integrate $e^{ax}\sin bx$ and $e^{ax}\cos bx$.

Let $K=\int e^{ax}\sin bx\,dx$ and $L=\int e^{ax}\cos bx\,dx$.

Then $\displaystyle\int e^{ax}\sin bx\,dx = \frac{e^{ax}}{a}\sin bx$

$$-\frac{b}{a}\int e^{ax}\cos bx\,dx.$$

And $\displaystyle\int e^{ax}\cos bx\,dx = \frac{e^{ax}}{a}\cos bx + \frac{b}{a}\int e^{ax}\sin bx\,dx,$

So that $aK + bL = e^{ax}\sin bx,$

and $-bK + aL = e^{ax}\cos bx.$

Solving for K and L we have

$$\int e^{ax}\sin bx\,dx = K = e^{ax}\,\frac{a\sin bx - b\cos bx}{a^2+b^2}$$

$$=\frac{e^{ax}}{\sqrt{(a^2+b^2)}}\sin\left(bx-\tan^{-1}\frac{b}{a}\right)$$

and $\int e^{ax} \cos bx\, dx = L = e^{ax} \dfrac{a \cos bx + b \sin bx}{a^2+b^2}$

$$= \frac{e^{ax}}{\sqrt{(a^2+b^2)}} \cos \left(bx - \tan^{-1} \frac{b}{a} \right)$$

(3) Integrate $x^2 e^x \operatorname{cox} x$.

From the last ex. we have

$$\int e^x \cos x\, dx = \frac{e^x}{\sqrt{2}} \cos \left(x - \frac{\pi}{4} \right)$$

Hence $\int x^2 e^x \cos x\, dx = \dfrac{x^2}{\sqrt{2}} e^x \cos \left(x - \dfrac{\pi}{4} \right)$

$$-\sqrt{2} \int x e^x \cos (x - \frac{\pi}{4})\, dx.$$

Now, $\int e^x \cos \left(x - \dfrac{\pi}{4} \right) dx = \dfrac{e^x}{\sqrt{2}} \cos (x - \pi)$

Hence $\int x^2 e^x \cos x\, dx = \dfrac{x^2}{\sqrt{2}} e^x \cos \left(x - \dfrac{\pi}{2} \right)$

$$-\sqrt{2} \left\{ \frac{x e^x}{\sqrt{2}} \cos \left(x - \frac{\pi}{4} \right) \frac{1}{\sqrt{2}} \int e^x \cos \left(x - \frac{\pi}{2}\, dx \right) \right\}$$

$$= \frac{a^2}{\sqrt{2}} e^x \cos \left(x - \frac{\pi}{4} \right) - x e^x \cos \left(x - \frac{\pi}{2} \right)$$

$$+ \frac{e^x}{\sqrt{2}} \cos \left(x - \frac{3\pi}{4} \right)$$

$$= \frac{x^2}{\sqrt{2}} e^x \cos \left(x - \frac{\pi}{4} \right) - x e^x \sin x$$

$$+\frac{e^x}{\sqrt{2}}\sin\left(x-\frac{\pi}{4}\right)$$

(4) Evaluate $\displaystyle\int_0^{4/4} \frac{e^{a\tan^{-1}x}}{(1+x^2)^{3/2}}\,dx$ (1955)

Let $\tan^{-1} x=\theta$, *i.e.*, $x=\tan\theta$,

so that $dx=\sec^2\theta\, d\theta$

Then $\displaystyle\int_0^{\pi} \frac{e^{a\tan^{-1}x}}{(1+x^2)^{3/2}}dx$

$$=\int_{x=0}^{x=\pi/4} \frac{e^{a\theta}}{\sec^3\theta}.\sec^2\theta\, dx$$

$$=\int_{x=0}^{x=\pi/4} e^{a\theta}\cos\theta\, d\theta=\left[\frac{e^{a\theta}(a\cos\theta+\sin\theta)}{1+a^2}\right]_{x=0}^{x=\pi/4}$$

$$=\frac{1}{1+a^2}\left\{\frac{a+x}{\sqrt{(1+x^2)}}e^{a\tan^{-1}x}\right\}_0^{\pi/4}$$

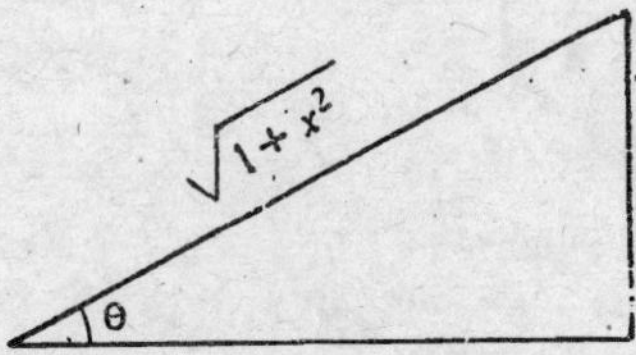

Fig. 19

$$=\frac{1}{1+a^2}\left\{\frac{a+\frac{1}{4}\pi}{\sqrt{(1+\frac{1}{16}\pi^2)}}e^{a\tan^{-1}\pi/4}-a\right\}$$

$$=\frac{1}{1+a^2}\left\{\frac{4a+\pi}{\sqrt{(16+\pi^2)}}e^{a\tan^{-1}\pi/4}-a\right\}.$$

If the limits were 0 and 1, the value would be

$$\frac{1}{1+a^2}\left\{\frac{a+1}{\sqrt{2}}e^{a}-a\right\}.$$

EXAMPLES XXVIII

Integrate

1. $xe^x \sin x$.
2. $x^2e^x \sin x$.
3. $e^{2x} \sin x \cos x$.
4. $e^{2x} \sin x \sin 3x$.
5. Evaluate $\displaystyle\int_1^e \frac{\cos \log x}{x} dx$.

(Banaras 1943)

Integrate

6. $\int \frac{x \sin^{-1} x}{\sqrt{(1-x^2)}} dx.$ 7. $\int \sec^{-1} x \, dx.$

8. $\int x \sec^{-1} x \, dx.$ 9. $\int \frac{x dx}{1+x^4}$

10. $\int \sin^{-1} \sqrt{\left[\frac{x}{a+x}\right]}$ 11. $\int \frac{dx}{x^2 \sqrt{(1+x^2)}}.$

12. $\int \frac{dx}{x^3 \sqrt{(x^2-1)}}$

13. $\int (a+b\, x^n)^m \, x^{n-1} \, dx.$

14. $\int \log \{x+(\sqrt{x^2+1})\} \, dx.$

15. $\int \frac{\tan x \, dx}{a+b \tan^2 x}.$

16. $\int \frac{dx}{a^2 \cos^2 x + b^2 \sin^2 x}$ (1957)

17. $\int \frac{x+\sin x}{1+\cos x} dx.$

CHAPTER X

PARTIAL FRACTIONS

III. Partial Fractions

(1) Integrate

$$\frac{1}{x^2-a^2}(x>a) \text{ and } \frac{1}{a^2-x^2} \quad (x<a).$$

$$\frac{1}{x^2-a^2}=\frac{1}{2a}\left(\frac{1}{x-a}-\frac{1}{x+a}\right)$$

$$\therefore \int\frac{dx}{x^2-a^2}=\frac{1}{2a}\int\frac{dx}{x-a}-\frac{1}{2a}\int\frac{dx}{x+a}$$

$$=\frac{1}{2a}\log\frac{x-a}{x+a}$$

$$\frac{1}{a^2-x^2}=\frac{1}{2a}\left(\frac{1}{a+x}+\frac{1}{a-x}\right)$$

$$\therefore \int\frac{dx}{a^2-x^2}=\frac{1}{2a}\int\frac{dx}{a+x}+\frac{1}{2a}\int\frac{dx}{a-x}$$

$$=\frac{1}{2a}\log\frac{a+x}{a-x}.$$

(2) Integrate $\dfrac{2x+3}{5x-8}$

$$\int\frac{2x+3}{5x-8}dx=\int\left\{\frac{2}{5}+\left(\frac{2x+3}{5x-8}-\frac{2}{5}\right)\right\}dx$$

$$=\frac{2}{5}\int dx+\frac{31}{5}\int\frac{dx}{5x-8}$$

$$=\frac{2x}{5}+\frac{31}{25}\log\ (5x-8).$$

(3) Integrate $\dfrac{1}{(x^2+1)(x^2+2)}$.

Let $$\frac{1}{(x^2+1)(x^2+2)}=\frac{A}{x^2+1}+\frac{B}{x^2+2}.$$

Then $1=A(x^2+2)+B(x+1)$
$\quad=(A+B)x^2+(2A+B).$

This is an identity. Hence, comparing coëfficients, we have

$$A+B=0, \qquad 2A+B=1$$

$$\therefore A=-B=1$$

$$\therefore \quad \frac{1}{(x^2+1)(x^2+2)}=\frac{1}{x^2+1}-\frac{1}{x^2+2}.$$

Hence $$\int\frac{dx}{(x^2+1)(x^2+2)}=\int\frac{dx}{x^2+1}-\int\frac{dx}{x^2+2}$$

$$=\tan^{-1}x-\frac{1}{\sqrt{2}}\tan^{-1}\frac{x}{\sqrt{2}}.$$

(4) Let $$\frac{1}{(x-1)(x-4)}=\frac{A}{x-1}+\frac{B}{x-4}.$$

Then $1=A(x-4)+B(x-1)$.

Being an identity this is true for all values of x. Hence, putting $x=1$, we see that $A=-\frac{1}{3}$; and putting $x=4$, we have $B=\frac{1}{3}$

$$\therefore \frac{1}{(x-1)(x-4)}=\frac{1}{3}\left(\frac{1}{x-4}-\frac{1}{x-1}\right)$$

$$\therefore \int\frac{dx}{(x-1)(x-4)}=\frac{1}{3}\int\frac{dx}{x-4}-\frac{1}{3}\int\frac{dx}{x-1}$$

$$=\frac{1}{3}\log\frac{x-4}{x-1}.$$

EXAMPLES XXIX

Integrate

1. $\dfrac{1}{x^2-9}$, $\dfrac{1}{4x^2-9}$, $\dfrac{1}{3x^2-11}$, $\dfrac{1}{11-3x^2}$.

2. $\dfrac{11x+2}{2x+11}$, $\dfrac{2-11x}{11-2x}$, $\dfrac{11x+2}{11-2x}$, $\dfrac{2-11x}{2x+11}$.

3. $\dfrac{1}{(x^2+4)(x^2+9)}$, $\dfrac{1}{(4-x^2)(x^2+25)}$,

$\dfrac{1}{(x^2+a^2)(x^2+b^2)}$.

4. $\dfrac{1}{(x-1)(x+7)}$, $\dfrac{1}{(3x+2)(3-x)}$,

$\dfrac{1}{(x-a)(x-b)}$, $\dfrac{1}{(2x-3)(5x-6)}$.

112. Solved Examples.

Integrate $\dfrac{2x+5}{4x^2-8x+13}$, $\dfrac{2x+5}{\sqrt{(4x^2-8x+13)}}$.

We know that the differential coefficient of $4x^2-8x+13$ is $8x-8$. Hence we shall split each of these fractions into two fractions such that in one of them the numerator may be $8x-8$. We have

$$2x+5=\tfrac{1}{4}(8x-8)+7$$

$$\therefore \int\frac{(2x+5)\,dx}{4x^2-8x+13}=\tfrac{1}{4}\int\frac{(8x-8)\,dx}{4x^2-8x+13}+7\int\frac{dx}{4x^2-8x+13}.$$

$$=\tfrac{1}{4}\log(4x^2-8x+13)+7\int\frac{dx}{4(x-1)^2+9}$$

$$=\tfrac{1}{4}\log(4x^2-8x+13)+\tfrac{7}{6}\tan^{-1}\frac{(2x-1)}{3}.$$

And $$\int\frac{(2x+5)dx}{\sqrt{(4x^2-8x+13)}}=\tfrac{1}{4}\int\frac{(8x-8)dx}{\sqrt{(4x^2-8x+13)}}$$

$$+7\int\frac{dx}{\sqrt{\{4(x-1)^2+9\}}}$$

$$=\tfrac{1}{4}\{2(\sqrt{4x^2-8x+13})\}+\tfrac{7}{2}\log[2(x-1)+\sqrt{\{4(x-1)^2+9\}}]$$

$$=\tfrac{1}{2}\sqrt{(4x^2-8x+13)}+\tfrac{7}{2}\log[2x-2+\sqrt{(4x^2-8x+13)}].$$

(2) Integrate $$\int\frac{dx}{(x-3)\sqrt{(x+1)}}.$$

Let $\sqrt{(x+1)}=y$, so that $x=y^2-1$.

Then $$\frac{dx}{2\sqrt{(x+1)}}=dy.$$

$\therefore$ The Integral$$=2\int\frac{dy}{y^2-4}=\tfrac{1}{2}\log\frac{y-2}{y+2}$$

$$=\tfrac{1}{2}\log\frac{\sqrt{(x+1)}-2}{\sqrt{(x+1)}+2}.$$

(3) Evaluate $\displaystyle\int^{3}\frac{x^3dx}{(x+1)(x+2)}$.

The expression under the integral sign

$$=\frac{x^3}{x^2+3x+2}$$

$$=\frac{x(x^2+3x+2)}{x^2+3x+2}-\frac{3x^2+2x}{x^2+3x+2}$$

$$=x-\frac{3(x^2+3x+2)}{x^2+3x+2}+\frac{7x+6}{x^2+3x+2}$$

$$=x-3+\tfrac{7}{2}\frac{2x+3}{x^2+3x+2}-\tfrac{9}{2}\cdot\frac{1}{x^2+3x+2}$$

$$=x-3+\tfrac{7}{2}\cdot\frac{2x+3}{x^2+3x+2}+\tfrac{9}{2}\left(\frac{1}{x+2}-\frac{1}{x+1}\right).$$

$\therefore$ The integral

$$=\left[\tfrac{1}{2}x^2-3x+\tfrac{7}{2}\log(x^2+3x+2)+\tfrac{9}{2}\log\frac{x+2}{x+1}\right]_2^3$$

$=[\frac{9}{2}-9+\frac{7}{2}\log 20+\frac{9}{2}\log\frac{5}{2}]-[2-6+\frac{7}{2}\log 12+\frac{9}{2}\log\frac{4}{3}]$
$=-\frac{1}{2}+8\log 5+\log 3-18\log 2.$

EXAMPLES XXX

Integrate

1. $\dfrac{5}{x^2-2x+10}$, $\dfrac{x+2}{x^2-2x+10}$, $\dfrac{1}{\sqrt{(x^2-2x+10)}}$, $\dfrac{x+2}{\sqrt{(x^2-2x+10)}}$.

2. $\dfrac{1}{3+2x-x^2}$, $\dfrac{5x+3}{3+2x-x^2}$, $\dfrac{1}{\sqrt{(3+2x-x^2)}}$, $\dfrac{5x+3}{\sqrt{(3+2x-x^2)}}$.

3. $\dfrac{1}{(x+1)\sqrt{(x-3)}}$.

4. $\dfrac{1}{(3x-4)\sqrt{(3x+5)}}$, $\dfrac{1}{(3x+14)\sqrt{(3x+5)}}$.

ANSWERS

EXAMPLES 1

(1) $-2, \ 3, 8.$ (2) $-1, 9, 21$

(3) $a+b, a+b, b, \dfrac{1}{a}+b, \ b(ab+1), \ b\left(\dfrac{b}{a}+1\right).$

(4) 11, 11. (5) $2, \dfrac{a+1}{a-1}, \ \dfrac{2a+1}{2a-1}.$

(6) (*i*) $2(x+h)+3$ (*ii*) $2h$ (*iii*) 2.

(7) (*i*) $(x+h)^2$ (*ii*) $h(2x+h)$ (*iii*) $2x+h$,

(8) 3^x sq. cm. (9) Yes, the function x^2.

(10) Yes, the function $6x$. (11) $\pm\sqrt{\tfrac{2}{5}}$.

EXAMPLES II

(1) No. (2) No. (3) Yes. (4) No.

(5) No. (6) No. (7) Yes. (8) Yes.

EXAMPLES III

1. $3p^2$ 2. 1 3. $-\frac{1}{8}$ 4. $\dfrac{2b-1}{1-b}$ 5. (1) $\dfrac{q}{p}$

(2) $\dfrac{p}{q}$ 6. (1) ∞ (2) a^2 7. $\frac{4}{3}$.

EXAMPLES IV

2. $\frac{p}{q}$ 3. 2 4. $-\log pq$. 5. $\frac{\log p}{\log q}$ 6. 0

7. $\frac{m}{p}$ 8. 3 9. 1.

EXAMPLES V

1. 2 2. p 3. $-\frac{1}{x^2}$ 4. $2ax$ 5. $\frac{1}{x^4}$

6. $\frac{x}{\sqrt{(x^2-a^2)}}$ 7. $-2b(a-bx)$ 8. $\frac{1}{2x}$

9. $2(at+b)$ 11. (*i*) -1 (*ii*) 0 12. The origin.

13. $(a\sqrt{2}, b), (-a\sqrt{2}, -b)$

14. (a) $2\cos 2x$ (b) $-e^{-x}$

EXAMPLES VI

1. $2\sqrt{x}(Y-y)=X-x$ 2. $Y-y=e^x(X-x)$
3. $Y-y+\sin x(X-x)=0$ 4. $2(X-x)+x^3Y=x$
5. $xX-yY=a^2$ 6. $\frac{xX}{a^2}-\frac{yY}{b^2}=1$
7. (*i*) $\frac{xX}{a^2}+\frac{yY}{b^2}=1$ (*ii*) $X-x=(1+x^2)(Y-y)$
8. $(0,1)$; $x+\sqrt{3}(y-1)=0$
9. $(\pm 2, \mp 2)$; $x-y=\pm 4$ 10. $x-2y+4=0$

EXAMPLES VII

1. (1) (0, 2) (2, −2) (2) (−1, −5)
2. (1) (−2, 0) (2) $(a, 0), (-a, 0)$
3. (1) Increasi- [illegible] ·en $x>5$; decreasing when $x<5$.

(2) Increasing when $x>2$ of <1 ; decreasing when $2>x>1$.

4. $\left(\frac{a}{\sqrt{2}}, \frac{a}{\sqrt{2}}\right)$, $\left(\frac{a}{\sqrt{2}}, -\frac{a}{\sqrt{2}}\right)$

$\left(-\frac{a}{\sqrt{2}}, \frac{a}{\sqrt{2}}\right)$, $\left(-\frac{a}{\sqrt{2}}-\frac{a}{\sqrt{2}}\right)$.

5. $(1,-1)$, $(-1, 5)$.

9. Parallel at $(0, b)$ and $(?, -b)$; perpendicular at $(a, 0)$ and $(-a, 0)$

10. $\left(-a, -\frac{a^2}{5c}\right)$ 11. $y-1=x$.

EXAMPLES VIII

1. (*i*) Concave upward when $x>1$; downward when $x<1$.

(*ii*) Concave upward when $x>3$ or $x<1$; downward when $3>x>1$.

7. $\frac{2}{3}\pi hr\ \delta r$ 8. ·06 in.

9. $2(at+b)$; $2(at+b)\ \delta t$, where δt is the small rise in temperature.

EXAMPLES IX

1. 2165 ft. per sec.
2. (1) 36 ft. per sec. (2) 8 secs. (3) 192 ft.
3. 1802 ft. per sec. 6. $u-ft; -f$.
9. (*a*) 30ft. per sec. (*b*) 180 ft. (c) 6 sec.
10, 242 m.p.h.

EXAMPLES X

1. $2x.\ 3x^2, 9x^8, \dfrac{1}{2\sqrt{x}}, -\tfrac{1}{2}x^{-3/2}, -\dfrac{3}{x^4}, -\tfrac{3}{4}x^{-7/4}, -\tfrac{2}{3}\ x^{-5/3}$

2. (1) $\dfrac{1}{x}$ (2) $\dfrac{a}{x}$ 3. (1) ae^{ax} (2) abe^{ax} (3) $-e^{-x}$

4. $2^x \log 2, 3^x \log 3, 2^{x+1} \log 2, 3^{5x} \log 3, (\tfrac{2}{3})^x$ (log 2 −log 3)

5. $\dfrac{1}{x} \log_2 e, \dfrac{1}{x} \log_{10} e, \dfrac{1}{x}$.

EXAMPLES XI

1. $2 \cos 2x$ 2. $-a \sin ax$ 3. $\dfrac{\sec^2 x}{2\sqrt{\tan x}}$ 4.

5. $\sin x + x \cos x$ 6. $\cos (x+h)$ 7. $\sin (x+b)$

8. $\dfrac{1}{a}\sec \dfrac{x}{a} \tan \dfrac{x}{a}$ 9. $n (x+a)^{n-1}$ 10. $\dfrac{a}{a^2+x^2}$

11. $-a \sin 2ax$ 12. $2 \sec^2 x \tan x$

13. $3e^{3x+2}$ 14. $2xe^{x^2}$

EXAMPLES XII

1. $2 \cos x - \sin x, e^x - \dfrac{1}{x} + 2x, \dfrac{1}{2\sqrt{x}},$

$x^3+x^2+x, \dfrac{2}{\sqrt{(1-x^2)}}, nx^{n-1}+a^n, 4x+1,$

$3x^2-2 (a+b+c) x+bc+ca+ab,\ 3a^2x^2+4\ abx+b^2$

2. (1) e^x (2) $\dfrac{1}{1+x}$ (3) $n(1+x)^{n-1}$

(4) $a^x \log a$

3. (1) $-\frac{1}{2}\left(\frac{a}{x^2}+1\right)$ (2) $\frac{2b(3-x)}{ax^3}$

(3) $-\frac{3a+2b\sqrt{x}}{2cx^2\sqrt{x}}$ (4) $\frac{bx\sqrt{x}-5a}{4cx^{9/4}}$

(5) $\frac{ax-b}{2x^{3/2}}$

EXAMPLES XIII

1. $x(2\cos x-x\sin x)$, $x^2(x+3)e^x$, $x^{n-1}(x+n)e^x$, $2^x(\cos x+\sin x\log 2)$, $x(1+2\log x)$,

$(\log x+1)\sin^{-1}x+\frac{x}{\sqrt{(1-x^2)}}\log x$,

$x\,e^x\{(x+2)\tan x+x\sec^2 x\}$,

$\frac{1}{2\sqrt{x}}\{\sec x\operatorname{cosec} x+2x(\sec^2 x-\operatorname{cosec}^2 x)\}$.

2. $x\operatorname{cosec} x(2-x\cot x)$, $-\operatorname{cosec} x\cot x$,

$-\frac{x\sin x-4\cos x}{x^5}$, $x^2(3\cot x-x\operatorname{cosec}^2 x)$,

$\frac{c^2(\sin x-x\cos x-x^2)}{(x^2+\sin x)^2}$, $xe^{-x}(2\cos x-x\sin x-x\cos x)$,

$\frac{(\log x-x)\sin x-x\log x(\sin x+\cos x)}{(\log x)^2\sin^2 x}e^{-x}$,

$\frac{3\sec x(2x\tan x-1)}{2x\sqrt{x}}$

3. $x\,(2\log x+1)-\dfrac{2}{\sqrt{x}}(\log\,x+2)$,

$e^x(\sec^2x+\tan x+\cos x-\sin x)$, $(x^2+3x+1)\,e^x\log x(1+x)e^x$, $\sec x$

$\{8\;e^x(\tan x+1)+3\tan x\}$, $5(\log x+1)-3e^x(\log x+\dfrac{1}{x})$, $x\cos x$.

4. $\dfrac{2x(\sin x+\cos x)-x^2(\cos x-\sin x)}{1+\sin 2x}$, $\dfrac{-2\sec x}{(\sec x+\tan x)^2}$,

$\dfrac{(\sin x+2)\{(x+1)\;e^x+3\}-x(e^x+3)\cos x}{(\sin x+2)^2}$

5. $-\dfrac{2a}{(a+x)^2}$, $\dfrac{2a}{(a-x)^2}$, $\dfrac{ad-bc}{(cx+d)^2}$,

$\dfrac{2}{\sin 2x-1}$, $\dfrac{2}{1+\sin 2x}$

6. $\dfrac{4a^2x}{(x^2+a^2)^2}$, $\dfrac{4(1-3x^2)}{(1-2x+3x^2)^2}$, $-\dfrac{1}{\sqrt{x}(\sqrt{x}-1)^2}$,

$\dfrac{x^2+2x-1}{x^2+2x+1}$, $\dfrac{(p-r)\;[qx^2+2\,(p+r)x+q]}{(rx^2+qx+p)^2}$

7. $\cos^2x-x\sin 2x$, $2\sin x\,(\sin\,x+2x\cos x)$,

$e^x\left[\dfrac{\cos^2x}{x}+\log x\cos^2x-\log x\sin 2x\right]$

EXAMPLES XIV

1. $-\frac{1}{2}\,(\sin x+3\sin 3x)$, $-\dfrac{\sin\sqrt{x}}{2\sqrt{x}}$

$-\cos\,x\,(\cos\,x-2x\,\sin\,x)$, $e^x\cos\,(e^x)$.

2. $\dfrac{-8}{(2x+3)^5}$, $na\,(ax+b)^{n-1}$

3. $\dfrac{2x+a}{2\sqrt{(x^2+ax+1)}}$, $-\frac{1}{2}\cdot\dfrac{2ax+b}{(ax^2+bx+c)^{3/2}}$

4. $(m\cos^2 x-n\sin^2 x)\sin^{m-1}x\cos^{n-1}x$;

$-\sin x\sec^2(\cos x)\cos[\tan(\cos x)]$

5. $-\dfrac{\sin\log x}{x}$, $-\dfrac{1}{x}\sin\log x\cos(\cos\log x)$,

$\dfrac{1}{x^2\log x}(1-\log x\log\log x)$.

6. $-\dfrac{1}{1+x^2}$, $-\frac{1}{2}e^{\sqrt{\cos x}}\cos^{-1/2}x\sin x$,

$\dfrac{1-x\sqrt{(1-x^2)}}{(1-x^2)^{3/2}}$, $-\frac{1}{2}$

7. $\dfrac{14(2x-1)}{(3x+2)^2}$, $\dfrac{3}{2\sqrt{x}}\left(x+\dfrac{1}{x}-2\right)\left(1+\dfrac{1}{x}\right)$

$\dfrac{an\,x^{n-1}}{(a+x)^{n+1}}$.

8. $\dfrac{2ab}{a^2-b^2x^2}$, $-\sqrt{(x^2-1)}$, $(3x^2+2x)\log x+x^2+x+\dfrac{1}{x}$

9. $2^{x\sin x}\log 2\,(\sin x+x\cos x)$,

$\dfrac{\cos\sqrt{x}\sin\sqrt{(\sin\sqrt{x})}}{8\sqrt{x}\sqrt{(\sin\sqrt{x})}\sqrt{\{\cos\sqrt{(\sin\sqrt{x})}\}}}$, $\dfrac{x^2-1}{x^2-4}$

EXAMPLES XV

1. $(ax+b)^{cx+d-1}\{c(ax+b)\log(ax+b)+a(cx+d)\}$,

$(\cos x)^x(\log\cos x-x\tan x)$, $e^{x\sin x}(\sin x+x\cos x)$.

2. $(\cos^{-1}x)^{x-1}\left\{\cos^{-1}x\log(\cos^{-1}x)-\dfrac{x}{\sqrt{(1-x^2)}}\right\}$,

$x^{\cos^{-1}x}\left\{\dfrac{\cos^{-1}x}{x}-\dfrac{\log x}{\sqrt{(1-x^2)}}\right\}$,

$\frac{1}{2}e^x x^{1/2}e^x\left(\log x+\dfrac{1}{x}\right)$, $x^x(\log x+1)e^{x^x}$

3. $(\sec x)^{\tan x}(\sec^2 x\log\sec x+\tan^2 x)$

$+(\tan x)^{\sec x}\sec x(\tan x\log\tan x+\sec x\operatorname{cosec} x)$,

$(\cos x)^x(\log\cos x-x\tan x)+x^{\cos x}\left(\dfrac{\cos x}{x}-\sin x\log x\right)$

4. $x^{x^2+1}(2\log x+1)+2x^{2x}(\log x+1)$,

$(1+\cos x)^{\sin x}\{\cos x\log(1+\cos x)-2\sin^2\frac{1}{2}x\}$.

5. $\cos x\, e^{\sin x}\log\tan x+\sec x\operatorname{cosec} x\, e^{\sin x}$

EXAMPLES XVI

1. e^b-e^a 2. $e^{-a}-e^{-b}$

3. $\frac{1}{2}(b^2-a^2)$ 4. $3\frac{3}{4}$ 5. 1

EXAMPLES XVII

1. $\dfrac{c}{b}$ 2. $\dfrac{a\pi}{2b}$ 3. 10 4. $x=2a$

5. $\frac{1}{2}h^2 \tan\alpha$ 6. $\dfrac{a^2-b^2}{3}$.

EXAMPLES XVIII

1. $2a\pi d^2$ 2. $\dfrac{\pi^2 c^2}{4b}$ 3. $\dfrac{\pi(e^{4b}-e^{4a})}{4}$

4. $\dfrac{\pi}{3}c^2$ 5. $\dfrac{\pi}{3}h^2 \tan^2\alpha$ 6. $\frac{4}{3}\pi ab^2$, $\frac{4}{3}\pi a^2 b$

EXAMPLES XIX

1. $10\frac{1}{2}$ 2. $\frac{1}{21}$ 3. $2(\sqrt{2}-1)$ 4. 1

5. -1 6. log 2 7. -1 8. $\frac{1}{2}\pi$

9. $\dfrac{b^2-a^2}{2}+\cos b-\cos a$.

EXAMPLES XX

1. e^x 2. $-\sqrt{x}$ 3. $-\dfrac{1}{22(11x+4)^2}$

4. $\frac{1}{12}(2-3x)^{-4}$ 5. $-\dfrac{a}{b}\cos bx$ and $\dfrac{a}{b}\sin bx$

6. $3y=2x^3$ 7. $\tan\left(x+\dfrac{\pi}{4}\right)$ 8. $\dfrac{\pi}{6}$

EXAMPLES XXI

1. $s=t^2+11t$. 2. $1704\frac{4}{11}$ miles

5. $b^2s+a \sin bt=0$.

EXAMPLES XXII

1. $y=\tan x+1$ 2. $1-\cos x$ 3. $(y+1)e^x=3$

4. $s=at^2+bt+c$ 5. $t(s-3t)=1$.

EXAMPLES XXIII

1. $\dfrac{x^{244}}{244}$, $-\frac{3}{8}x^{-8/3}$, $\dfrac{x^{c+1}}{c+1}$.

2. $\frac{2}{195}(15x-2)^{13/2}$, $-\frac{2}{195}(2-15x)^{13/2}$

$-\frac{2}{135}(15x-2)^{-9/2}$, $\frac{2}{135}(2-15x)^{-9/2}$, $-\dfrac{(a-bx)^{n+1}}{(n+1)b}$.

3. $-\dfrac{1}{a}\log(b-ax)$, $-\dfrac{1}{b}\log(a-bx)$, $-\dfrac{2}{5\sqrt{(5x+2)}}$.

4. $\frac{2}{3}(e^x+\log x)^{3/2}$, $\dfrac{(ax^2+bx+c)^{n+1}}{n+1}$, $\dfrac{(c-bx-ax^2)^{n+1}}{n+1}$.

5. $\log(ax^2+bx+c)$, $\log x$, $\log(\log x)$, $\dfrac{-2}{\sqrt{(x^2+3x-2)}}$

6. $\log(e^x+e^{-x})$, $\log \sin^{-1} x$, $\log \cot x$ 7. $-\frac{1}{3}\sin^{-3}x$

8. $\frac{2}{3}(\sqrt{2}-1)$. 9. $\frac{1}{30}(5x^2-10x+17)^3$.

EXAMPLES XXIV

1. $\frac{1}{2}x^2+e^x$, $\frac{1}{3}x^3-\log x$, $\dfrac{a}{2}x^2-\dfrac{b}{x}$, $\frac{1}{3}ax^3+\frac{1}{2}bx^2+cx$.

2. $\frac{1}{2}(x+\sin x\cos x)$, $\frac{1}{12}\cos 3x-\frac{3}{4}\cos x$, $\frac{1}{4}-\frac{1}{4}\cos 2x$,

$\frac{1}{2}\left[\dfrac{\sin(m-n)x}{m-n}-\dfrac{\sin(m+n)x}{m+n}\right]$.

3. $\dfrac{1}{n+1}\sin^{n+1}x$; $\frac{1}{5}\tan^5 x$, $-\frac{1}{2}(\operatorname{cosec}^{-1} x)$.

4. $x-a\log(x+a)$, $x+a\log x$,
$-a\log(a-x)-x$, $a\log x-x$.

5. $-\left(\dfrac{a}{x}+\dfrac{b}{2x}+\dfrac{c}{3x^3}\right)$, $\dfrac{b}{x}-\dfrac{c}{2x^2}-a\log x$,

$\frac{1}{2}\tan^{-1}\dfrac{x-3}{2}$, $\frac{1}{4}\tan^{-1}\dfrac{2x-1}{2}$.

6. $\log(e^x+11)$, $\log(\log\sec x)$, $\dfrac{4^x}{\log 4}+\frac{1}{4}x^4$.

7. $\frac{1}{11}\sec^{-1}\dfrac{x}{11}$, $\text{vers}^{-1}\dfrac{x}{3}$ 8. $\dfrac{\pi}{4}$ 9. $\frac{2}{3}$.

EXAMPLES XXV

1. $a\sin e^x$, $e^{\tan^{-1}x}$, $\frac{1}{3}\tan^{-1}(x^3)$

2. $-\dfrac{\sqrt{(1-x)}}{\sqrt{(1+x)}}$ 3. $-\frac{1}{4}$ 4. $\frac{1}{4}$ 5. $\dfrac{\pi}{2}$ 6. $\dfrac{\pi}{4}$

EXAMPLES XXVI

1. $\dfrac{1}{a}\log(\sec ax+\tan ax)$, $\dfrac{1}{a}\log\tan\dfrac{ax}{2}$.

2. $-\frac{1}{8}(\cot x)^8$, $\frac{1}{7}(\tan x)^7$.

3. $\log[x+\sqrt{(x^2-4)}]$, $\sin^{-1}\dfrac{x}{2}$, $\log[x+(\sqrt{x^2+4})]$,

$\dfrac{x\sqrt{(x^2+4)}}{2}+2\log[x+\sqrt{(x^2+4)}]$,

$\dfrac{x\sqrt{(x^2-4)}}{2}-2\log[x+\sqrt{(x^2-4)}]$

$\dfrac{x\sqrt{(4-x^2)}}{2}+2\sin^{-1}\dfrac{x}{2}$.

4. $\log [x-2+\sqrt{(x^2-4x+5)}]$,

$$(x-2)\frac{\sqrt{(x^2-4x+5)}}{2}+\tfrac{1}{2}\log [x-2+\sqrt{(x^2-4x+5)}],$$

$$\sin^{-1}\frac{x-3}{4},\quad \frac{(x-3)\sqrt{(7+6x-x^2)}}{2}+8\sin^{-1}\frac{x-3}{4}.$$

5. $\frac{1}{3}a^3$. 6. $\tan x - \cot x$, $\frac{1}{b}\log (a+b\sin x)$.

7. $\dfrac{(3x^2-2a^2)^{p+1}}{6(p+1)}$, $\log (x-\sin x)$, $\log (xe^x+3)$.

8. $\sqrt{(2x+1)}$, $\frac{1}{3}(2x-5)\sqrt{(2x+1)}$,

$\frac{1}{2}\sqrt{(4x^2-1)}-\frac{1}{2}\log [2x+\sqrt{(4x^2-1)}]$

9. $\dfrac{1}{\sqrt{2}}\log\tan\left(\dfrac{x}{2}-\dfrac{\pi}{8}\right)$,

$$\frac{1}{\sqrt{(a^2+b^2)}}\log\tan\left(\frac{x}{2}+{}^{1}\tan^{-1}\frac{a}{b}\right).$$

10. $\tan x - x$, $\frac{1}{2}\tan^2 x-\log\sec x$,

$x-\tan x+{}^{1}\tan^3 x$, $\frac{1}{3}\sec^3 x-\sec x$

11. $\log (\log x)$, $\log [\log (\log x)]$. 12. $x-\log (1+e^x)$.

13. $\frac{1}{3}$ 14. $\sqrt{2}-1$. 15. (*i*) $\frac{\pi}{2}$ (*ii*) $\sqrt{2}-1$ (*iii*) 1.

EXAMPLES XXVII

1. $\sin x - x\cos x$, $(x^2-2)\sin x+2x\cos x$,

$$\frac{x^2}{4}-\frac{1}{4}x\sin 2x-\frac{1}{8}\cos 2x,$$

$\frac{x^3}{6} - \frac{x^2}{8}\sin 4x - \frac{x}{16}\cos 4x + \frac{1}{32}\sin 4x.$

2. $\frac{1}{4}(2x^2-2x+1)e^{2x}$, $(x^3-3x^2+6x-6)e^x$,
$\frac{1}{27}(9x^3-9x^2+6x-2)e^{3x}$, $\frac{1}{8}(4x^3-6x^2+6x-3)e^{2x}$.

3. $x(\log x-1)$, $\frac{x^2}{4}(2\log x-1)$, $\frac{x^3}{9}(3\log x-1)$

$\frac{x^{n+1}}{(n+1)^2}[(n+1)\log x-1]$

4. $\frac{2}{3}\sin^3 x$, $(2-x^2)\cos x+2x\sin x$,
$\frac{1}{4}x\sin 2x+\frac{1}{8}\cos 2x-\frac{1}{8}x\sin 4x-\frac{1}{32}\cos 4x$.

5. $x\tan^{-1}x-\frac{1}{2}\log(1+x^2)$, $\frac{1}{2}\{(x^2+1)\tan^{-1}x-x\}$,
$\frac{1}{4}(2x^2-1)\sin^{-1}x+\frac{1}{4}x\sqrt{(1-x)}$,
$\frac{x^3}{3}\sin^{-1}x+\frac{1}{3}\sqrt{(1-x^2)}-\frac{1}{9}(1-x)^{3/2}$.

6. 1, $\frac{\pi}{4\sqrt{2}}+\frac{1}{\sqrt{2}}-1$, π. 7. 1, 2 8. $\frac{1}{2}(\log x)^2$

EXAMPLES XXVIII

1. $\frac{xe^x}{\sqrt{2}}\sin\left(x-\frac{\pi}{4}\right)+\frac{1}{2}e^x\cos x$.

2. $\frac{x^2e^x}{\sqrt{2}}\sin\left(x-\frac{\pi}{4}\right)+xe^x\cos x-\frac{1}{\sqrt{2}}e^x\cos\left(x-\frac{\pi}{4}\right)$

3. $\frac{1}{4\sqrt{2}}e^{2x}\sin\left(2x-\frac{\pi}{4}\right)$

4. $e^{2x}\left\{\frac{\cos 2x+\sin 2x}{8}-\frac{\cos 4x+2\sin 4x}{20}\right\}$.

5. $\sin 1^{e}$ 6. $x-\sqrt{(1-x)}\sin^{-1}x.$

7. $x\sec^{-1}x-\log[x+(\sqrt{x}-1)]$

8. $\frac{x^2}{2}\sec^{-1}x-\frac{1}{2}\sqrt{(x-1)}.$ 9. $\frac{1}{2}\tan^{-1}x^3$

10. $(a+x)\tan^{-1}\sqrt{\left[\frac{x}{a}\right]}-\sqrt{ax}.$ 11. $-\frac{\sqrt{(1+x^2)}}{x}$

12. $\frac{1}{2}\sec^{-1}x+\frac{\sqrt{(x^2-1)}}{2x^2},$ 13. $\frac{(a+bx^n)^{m+1}}{n(m+1)b}.$

14. $x\log[x+\sqrt{(x^2+1)}-\sqrt{(x^2+1)}]$

15. $\frac{1}{2(b-a)}\log(a\cos^2x+b\sin^2x).$

16. $\frac{1}{ab}\tan^{-1}\left(\frac{b}{a}\tan x\right).$ 17. $x\tan\frac{x}{2}$

EXAMPLES XXIX

1. $\frac{1}{6}\log\frac{x-3}{x+3},$ $\frac{1}{12}\log\frac{2x-3}{2x+3}$

$\frac{1}{2\sqrt{33}}\log\frac{x\sqrt{3}-x\sqrt{11}}{x\sqrt{3}+x\sqrt{11}},$ $\frac{1}{2\sqrt{33}}\log\frac{\sqrt{11}+x\sqrt{3}}{\sqrt{11}-x\sqrt{3}}$

2. $\frac{11}{2}x-\frac{117}{4}\log(2x+11),$ $\frac{11}{2}x+\frac{117}{4}\log(11-2x),$

$\frac{125}{4}\log\frac{1}{11-2x}-\frac{11}{2}x,$ $\frac{125}{4}\log(2x+11)-\frac{11}{2}x.$

3. $\frac{1}{10}\tan^{-1}\frac{x}{2}-\frac{1}{15}\tan^{-1}\frac{x}{3},$

$\frac{1}{29}\left\{\frac{1}{4}\log\frac{2+x}{2-x}+\frac{1}{5}\tan^{-1}\frac{x}{5}\right\}$

$$\frac{1}{a^2-b^2}\left\{\frac{1}{b}\tan^{-1}\frac{x}{b}-\frac{1}{a}\tan^{-1}\frac{x}{a}\right\}$$

4. $\frac{1}{8}\log\frac{x-1}{x+7},\ \frac{1}{11}\log\frac{(3x+2)}{3-x}$

$$\frac{1}{a-b}\log\frac{x-a}{x-b},\ \frac{1}{3}\log\frac{2x-3}{5x-6}.$$

EXAMPLES XXX

1. $\frac{1}{3}\tan^{-1}\frac{x-1}{3},\ \frac{1}{2}\log(x^2-2x+10)+\tan^{-1}\frac{x-1}{3},$

$\log[x-1+\sqrt{(x^2-2x+10)}],$

$\sqrt{(x^2-2x+10)}+3\log[x-1+\sqrt{(x^2-2x+10)}].$

2. $\frac{1}{4}\log\frac{1+x}{3-x},\ \log\frac{1}{\sqrt{[(3-x)^9(1+x)]}},$

$\sin^{-1}\frac{x-1}{2},\ 8\sin^{-1}\frac{x-1}{2}-5\sqrt{(3+2x-x^2)}$

3. $\tan^{-1}\frac{\sqrt{(x-3)}}{2}$

4. $\frac{1}{3}\log\frac{\sqrt{(3x+5)}-3}{\sqrt{(3x+5)}+3},\ \frac{2}{3}\tan^{-1}\frac{\sqrt{(3x+5)}}{3}$